Litigation: The Views of Midwives and Obstetricians

Who's Accountable? Who's to Blame?

Andrew Symon
RGN, RM, MA (Hons), PhD

Hochland & Hochland Ltd

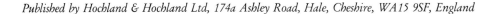

Published by Hochland & Hochland Ltd, 174a Ashley Road, Hale, Cheshire, WA15 9SF, England

© Andrew Symon 1998

First Edition

ISBN 1 898507 67 8

British Library Catalouging in Publication Data
A catalogue record for this book is availabe from the British Library

Typeset By Carnegie Publishing Limited.
Printed in Great Britain

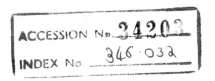

Contents

List of Figures

List of Tables

Appendices

Acknowledgements

This research constituted part of a PhD undertaken at the University of Edinburgh from 1993 to 1997. Thanks are due to my two academic supervisors, Professor Michael Adler and Professor Kath Melia, who provided invaluable advice and support. Without their encouragement and unfailing good humour throughout the period of my thesis, the task of conducting the research reported here would have been immeasurably more difficult.

This book is the result of two surveys, one of midwives, the other of obstetricians. The midwifery survey was funded by the National Board for Nursing, Midwifery and Health Visiting for Scotland (NBS) through the Margaret Callum Rodger award in 1994. This survey was organized and sent by the Edinburgh office of the Royal College of Midwives, which also allowed the use of their address for the return of the questionnaires. Special thanks go to Patty Purton and Helen Henderson for coordinating this.

The obstetric survey was funded by the Economic and Social Research Council (ESRC), which began the funding of part-time postgraduate studentships in 1993. This paid for University fees and contributed to other research costs including those of the obstetric survey. The supervision of Dr Martin Lees of the Simpson Memorial Maternity Pavilion in Edinburgh was essential, and my thanks also go to Professor William Dunlop, Honorary President of the Royal College of Obstetricians and Gynaecologists in London, who allowed the RCOG address to be used as a 'post box' for the return of questionnaires.

The surveys relied on the willingness to cooperate on the part of many midwives and doctors, and their contributions, frequently of sensitive information, are duly acknowledged. Without these respondents there would be no results to publish.

Study time (equivalent to one day a week) was allowed by the Perth and Kinross NHS Healthcare Trust from July 1994, and this allowed valuable time for the analysis of the two thousand questionnaires which were returned.

Lastly I would like to thank my wife Maggie: for conspiring with Mike Adler in the first instance to persuade me that studying for a PhD was a good idea; for being flexible in creating the time and space to allow me to carry out the necessary work; and for producing Jamie and David during the course of the research. While their direct input has been minimal, they have provided a degree of distraction which has on occasion been invaluable.

Introduction

It appears – although supporting evidence has been scanty – that there has been a significant increase in medical negligence litigation (and especially obstetric litigation) over the last 10–15 years. This has been blamed for a number of apparent side-effects, including a rise in defensive medicine, lowered recruitment to obstetrics, and a setting aside of a significant proportion of the health budget to pay damages awards and insurance premiums against further potential damages. Part of the problem in trying to analyse the possible effects of this phenomenon is that until very recently there was no systematic central collation of incidents of perinatal litigation in either Scotland or England, or, for that matter, any local collations which were published. Without adequate publicly-available knowledge, the debate about the extent of litigation and the consequent use of public funds, and about what constitutes a justified response to the fear or prospect of litigation, is at best ill-informed.

The research reported here constituted part of a large scale investigation into perinatal litigation, undertaken as a PhD at the University of Edinburgh (Symon, 1997a). Essentially the research followed two distinct lines of enquiry. The first was an examination of several hundred obstetric/midwifery legal files in Scotland and two identified English areas, in which allegations of negligence had been made; the second, reported here, concerned two large scale surveys of obstetricians and midwives.

For the first time the views of a large number of clinical practitioners are presented in an attempt to develop the debate about litigation in this area of health care. It should be borne in mind that these views have not been informed by widely-available and comprehensive data concerning either the incidence or nature of litigation, although it is hoped that, with the conclusion of the research into legal files, this deficiency will be redressed in the near future. Practitioners (this term is used to denote both obstetricians and midwives) throughout Scotland and in the two English areas were identified, and their perceptions of and attitudes towards litigation explored. Given the claims made by certain authors about the scale and particularly the effects of litigation, it is important to record the views of those who work in this field to see if these claims are justified. Doing so in the scale reported here allows for some conclusions to be drawn about the perceptions of the 'front line' clinical staff against whom allegations may be made.

The survey: a summary

Details about the midwifery and obstetric surveys, and the characteristics of the respondents, can be found in, respectively, Appendices A and B. Those targeted were all Scottish members of the Royal College of Midwives (RCM), and all identified midwives in the two English areas in which analysis of legal files took place. Similarly with the obstetricians, all known practising clinicians in Scotland and the two English areas were approached, as were a number of 'GP obstetricians' in Scotland. 1790 midwives and 211 obstetricians responded, the return rates being respectively 51%[1] and 63%. Some interesting cross-border differences of opinion were noted, particularly in the larger midwifery survey, and these are described in the text. Details about the pairing of midwifery respondents from Scotland and England can be found in Appendix A. Rather than referring repeatedly to English-based and Scottish-based practitioners, for ease of reading I refer instead to English and Scottish practitioners. I apologize if this offends anyone's national sensibilities (in whichever direction).

The questionnaires were essentially the same, although some questions were directed specifically at obstetricians, and others at midwives, so they were not identical. Both were divided into four parts, which are followed in this book. The back of the midwifery survey was left blank, and respondents were invited to add comments. One midwife included three sheets entitled 'The ramblings of a geriatric midwife'. This very interesting account of changes in midwifery over the years can be found in Appendix C.

Part I concerns litigation in a general sense. Chapter 1 sets the scene by discussing accountability and compensation, medical negligence within its legal context, and claims about the incidence of litigation. In Chapter 2 the views of respondents regarding the perceived incidence of and reasons for litigation are detailed, and there is a short discussion of no fault compensation, which has been advocated as a possible solution to the apparent litigation 'crisis'. Chapter 3 examines the personal involvement in litigation of the respondents, and Chapter 4 explores the possible effects on clinical practice of litigation (or the fear of litigation).

In Part II attitudes towards the normality of pregnancy are examined. Chapter 5 explores the degree of responsibility enjoyed by midwives, as well as the desire among midwives to work in a midwife-run unit (MRU). Chapter 6 looks at patient autonomy, and questions the weight accorded to a patient's expressed preference, particularly when this relates to minimal intervention. Lastly there is a discussion of the views of practitioners towards home birth.

Part III concerns the labour period, which has been seen to be the focus of much (although not all) of the litigation in obstetrics/midwifery. Chapter 7 explores the question of supervision, which has been highlighted as an area of deficiency in suboptimal outcomes; it also continues the theme of patient autonomy, looking explicitly at episiotomy. Chapter 8 develops the theme of fetal monitoring, which has formed the basis of many legal actions. The frequency, desirability, and safety of electronic monitoring are all examined, as is the perceived ability of practitioners to interpret fetal compromise in cardiotocograph (CTG) tracings.

Part IV looks at communication, complaints and counselling procedures. Chapter 9

---

1 Midwives are allegedly reluctant to respond to postal surveys, and I have been informed that 51% is quite a respectable rate.

assesses the degree of communication and rapport between obstetrician and midwife, and between staff and patient, while Chapter 10 examines how staff deal with poor outcomes and complaints. The role of 'consumer groups' is also examined.

In Chapter 11 there is a discussion both of this research and of other findings concerning obstetric and midwifery practice, and some suggestions for further investigation are made.

The surveys presented here allow the discussion of the perceived effect of litigation to move on. Because of the large scale of the surveys, reasonable certainty about the views of clinical practitioners can be assumed, for the Scottish respondents at least. However, it is acknowledged that a postal survey, largely comprising 'closed answer' questions, is an imperfect method of detailing complex perceptions and beliefs, and further research is currently being undertaken by the author which explores this topic in a more in-depth and qualitative way. Since January 1997 there has been a series of articles in the British Journal of Midwifery (based on the examination of legal files) concerning certain aspects of perinatal litigation.

The discussion of subjects presented here is by no means intended to be the definitive version. Only a brief introduction to each topic is given, with references for those who wish to explore the subject in more depth. The purpose here is to introduce the subject, and describe the views of practitioners, so allowing some of the claims made in the literature to be assessed in the light of a large scale survey. The views may also be taken as the starting point for further exploration and research.

Throughout the book reference is made to the numbers of respondents answering questions in a particular way. When mention is made of the proportion of the entire midwifery or obstetric sample, or of any of their sub-groups, percentage figures have been rounded either up or down to the nearest percentage point, except for the smaller figures. In some of the figures the abbreviation 'NAND' is used: this stands for 'Neither Agree Nor Disagree'.

A note about terminology: in the midwifery questionnaire I used a variety of terms to denote a pregnant woman or newly-delivered mother. However, in this book, as in the obstetric questionnaire, I have used the term 'patient', and some readers will dislike this. The word has unfortunate connotations (critics claim it connotes sickness when pregnancy and labour are essentially normal physiological life events), but it is at least widely used and universally understood. Most of the alternative terms can be criticised for being either too cumbersome ('user of maternity services') or inappropriate. While 'client' is undoubtedly gaining currency, I feel this connotes a fee-for-service relationship which, like 'customer', ought not to apply in health care. I acknowledge the deficiencies of 'patient', and indeed have enjoyed a stimulating correspondence with a lecturer who criticised my use of this term in an article. I am not convinced that the term 'client' represents an improvement, and so am reluctant to jump out of the patient's frying pan into the client's fire merely for the sake of change.

Part 1
Litigation Generally

CHAPTER ONE

Setting the Scene

There appears to be a strong perception that medical negligence litigation, and especially obstetric litigation, has increased sharply in recent years. This apparent belief has been accompanied by claims that clinical practice has changed as a result, and yet it seems that little has been done to verify this belief, or to describe or quantify these alterations in clinical conduct. This chapter sets the scene, describing briefly the notion of accountability and the law of medical negligence, and discussing some of the claims made in the literature concerning litigation. It is not within the remit of this chapter to set out the definitive version of the law of negligence: this has already been adequately covered in standard medical and midwifery texts (Powers and Harris, 1995; Dimond, 1994).

Accountability and compensation

In a modern democracy accountability is highly prized: our elected leaders and many of those in positions of power are held to be answerable for their actions. Greenfield (1975) notes that accountability is an *ex post* concept, it is retrospective; yet as Etzioni (1975) points out, it is not always equally applied – those groups with higher status or more power are able to make any system more accountable to them.

It is well recognized that those in the health professions are accountable to those who use their services. The General Medical Council sums this up: 'The primary concerns are to protect the public and to uphold the reputation of the medical profession' (GMC, 1989). The United Kingdom Central Council for Nursing, Midwifery and Health Visiting states that the practitioner 'should recognize that the interests of public and patient must predominate over those of the practitioner and profession ... silently to tolerate poor standards is to act in a manner contrary to the interests of patients or clients, and thus to renege on personal professional accountability' (UKCC, 1989).

The issue of accountability within the health service has been increasingly stressed in recent years. Beech (1990) advocated a radical overhaul of the whole system of complaints, and stressed the need for hard principles of accountability. Initiatives such as the Patients' Charter have focused attention on the theory of clinical and managerial accountability, and have encouraged dissatisfied patients to make formal complaints. Many hospital Trusts now have a designated 'Complaints officer', and if a patient feels that redress has not been obtained in this way the Health Service Commissioner (Ombudsman) can investigate the matter. For many years the Ombudsman only had the power to investigate complaints not of a clinical nature; since 1996 this restriction has been lifted, although it will usually be required that a patient approach the hospital's own complaints system as a first step. Recent changes in the complaints framework mean that most complaints must be made within six months of the event in question (DoH, 1996).

A significant diminution of the potential for attaining universally-equable administrative justice has been the devolution of responsibility to local hospital Trusts, each of which can interpret guidelines on dealing with patient complaints as they see fit. Reid et al (1995) note the wide variation in such processes between different areas.

The process of accountability may be viewed as a pyramid, with initial (verbal or written) complaints at base level. The number of these which become official data is much smaller, and the number which reach the stage of formal enquiry smaller still (Reid et al, 1995). This research focused on those formal complaints which included allegations of clinical negligence, and sought the views of clinical staff to this phenomenon. Formal legal claims may be seen as a sub-set of the whole category of complaints: without official statistics which admit to the scale of complaints, it is impossible to know how large or small this sub-set is.

This research was concerned with allegations of negligence, and while these may be seen in terms of professional accountability, here they are examined from the point of view of the civil law. While professional accountability aims to ensure that the standards of a profession are maintained so that the general public benefits, and has confidence in it and so continues to accord it professional status, civil legal accountability aims to restore someone who has suffered loss through the negligence of another to the position they would have been in had that negligence not occurred.

Medical negligence

In this area of law the term 'medical' includes other areas of health care, among them midwifery and neonatal nursing. In this discussion both English and Scottish legal terms are used. The law of wrongs is known as 'tort' in England, and 'delict' in Scotland; similarly, 'plaintiff' and 'pursuer' are synonymous, as are 'defendant' and 'defender'.

Medical negligence is covered by the fault-based law of tort/delict. To prove negligence, i.e. to establish that the defendant/defender was at fault, the plaintiff/pursuer must satisfy three criteria: (s)he must prove that there was a duty of care owed by the defendant/defender; that there was a breach of this duty of care; and that damage resulted from the breach. The 'duty of care' principle (sometimes referred to as the 'good neighbour' principle) stems from the judgement given in the case of Donoghue v Stevenson,[1] where it was stated that a duty of care would be owed, for example, by me to 'persons who are so closely and directly affected by my acts that I ought reasonably to have them in contemplation as being so affected when I am directing my mind to the acts or omissions which are called in question' (from Lord Atkin's judgement). Brown (1985) comments: 'It should also be noted that the standard or degree of such

---

1 Donoghue v Stevenson, 1932 SC (HL) 31 ; 1932 SLT, 317

care will vary ... it will not be that of an outstanding specialist in a particular field of work ... unless a person sets himself or herself up as exercising such skill'.

The test for medical negligence in Scotland was laid down in the judgement by Lord President Clyde in Hunter v Hanley in 1955[2] : 'The true test for establishing negligence on the part of a doctor is whether he has been proven to be guilty of such failure as no doctor of ordinary skill would be guilty of if acting with ordinary care ... it must be established that the course the doctor adopted is one which no professional man of ordinary skill would have taken if he had been acting with ordinary care'. This position was reaffirmed in the case of Maynard v. West Midlands RHA[3] when the House of Lords held that in medicine there is room for a difference of opinion and practice, and that a court's preference for one body of opinion over another was no basis for a conclusion of negligence.

Hunter v Hanley, a Scottish case, was followed two years later in English law in the case of Bolam v Friern HMC.[4] In medico-legal text books the 'Bolam test', or 'Bolam principles', may be referred to, and while these do not properly refer to Scots law, it is usually accepted that in this area they are essentially the same. One jurist, however, believes that the Scottish and English tests for establishing an acceptable standard are slightly different. Howie (1983) claims that in Scotland the test for negligence (per Hunter v Hanley) is that *no* doctor of ordinary skill would have acted in the way alleged; in England the Bolam principle holds that the act is safe as long as it in accordance with *a responsible body of opinion*. In other words he is claiming that the test in Scotland is tougher than in England. Another (anonymous) writer echoes this point (1990): (s)he notes that in the case of Maynard Lord Scarman said 'I do not think that the words of Lord President Clyde in Hunter v Hanley can be bettered', but in the later case of Sidaway[5] referred to Bolam in detail, and tried to equate Scots law with Bolam principles. As the two are not exactly the same, this commentator claims that the law in England is 'in an unsatisfactorily fluid state'. It must be said that this distinction is not a problem which seems to have troubled most writers or judges since the two respective judgements, although the applicability of this test has recently been criticized (see the concluding chapter).

Liability cannot be inferred simply because something goes wrong. Lord Ross gave express approval of this in 1981: 'If medical and nursing staff were to be found liable when anything untoward occurred, that would have an adverse effect on the medical and nursing professions and on the public generally'.[6] Brazier (1987) picks up on this point of muzzling innovation: 'If liability in negligence automatically followed once harm resulted from the adoption of a novel method of treatment, medical progress would be stultified'.

---

2 Hunter v Hanley 1955 SC 200
3 Maynard v West Midlands RHA 1984 1 WLR 634
4 Bolam v Friern HMC 1957 2 All ER 118
5 Sidaway v Board of Governors of the Bethlem Royal Hospital and others, [1984] 2 WLR 778, CA
6 Rolland v Lothian Health Board, 1981 (unreported)

A legal dispute will often turn to the question of what should have happened in a particular case in order to see whether there might have been a breach of the duty of care. 'Expert opinions' may be sought to find out what the ordinary competent practitioner could be expected to do or know, and one of the hallmarks of a profession is that it reserves the right to decide just what is acceptable, as noted by Klein (1973: 3): 'It is for professional colleagues, not the user of the services, to judge the appropriateness and the competence of the skills applied'. This view does not go unchallenged, however: Norrie (1985) claims that medicine should be just as accountable as other occupations – 'It is nothing short of dangerous complacency to assume that they (doctors) are safe from legal criticism if they do only as their neighbours do'.

This view seemed to be backed up by the judgement in the case of Sidaway[7]: 'the definition of a duty of care is a matter for the law and the court ... in a word, the law will not permit the medical profession to play God'. Despite this courts appear to have been happy to accept, within the bounds of reasonableness, that in medical matters medical people are best placed to decide what is a satisfactory standard of care. A move to challenge this is discussed in Chapter 11.

A problem does however occur when 'expert witnesses' disagree with one another. In Whitehouse v Jordan[8] it was felt that 'expert opinion' must be seen to be the independent expert opinion of a specialist, and not partisan. 'While some degree of consultation between experts and legal advisers is entirely proper, it is necessary that expert evidence presented to the court should be, and should be seen to be, the independent product of the expert uninfluenced as to form or content by the exigencies of litigation. To the extent that it is not, the evidence is likely to be not only incorrect, but also self-defeating'.[9] This view was reinforced by the judge in Wisniewski v Central Manchester HA.[10] With reference to one of the defence experts he said: 'Professor Thomas' unwillingness to criticize was in my view unjustified and an example of his general disinclination to say much that might be adverse to the defendant's case'.

The test for medical negligence then is that there is such a low standard of care given by a health care professional to someone to whom a duty of care is owed, that no practitioner of reasonably competent ability could have given that care, and that damage results from this. Given that the professions themselves are able to determine what is a reasonable standard of care, the test might appear to be a very tough one. This may be seen as one of the benefits accruing to a profession – that it has a strong say in how it will be judged by the law.

---

7 Sidaway v Board of Governors of the Bethlem Royal Hospital and others, [1984] 2 WLR 778, CA (per Donaldson MR)
8 Whitehouse v Jordan and another [1981] 1 WLR 246 (H. L.) ; [1980] 1 All ER 650 C. A.
9 per Lord Wilberforce in the House of Lords, cited in the New Law Journal, Jan 1981, p 2
10 Wisniewski v Central Manchester HA [1996] 7 Med LR 248 (per Thomas J @ 262)

The incidence of litigation

How often patients sue has been the subject of research, speculation and comment for some time. My own research has identified the incidence and rate of perinatal litigation in Scotland and in two English areas since 1980 (Symon, personal data; unpublished).

In 1983 Howie claimed: 'One of the more notable developments in the field of medical law has been the marked increase in the number of actions brought against doctors and other health service staff for professional negligence'. Such received wisdom is difficult to verify: another writer comments that 'reliable accurate information as to the number of claims for damages, the success rate, the amounts paid and their mode of disposal is unfortunately unobtainable' (Blackie, 1985). This has not changed in more recent years: Tharmaratnam and Gillmer (1995) claim that 'Medical litigation in the 1980s increased sharply', but unfortunately provide no references or data to support this claim. Similarly Easterbrook (1996) asserts that 'there has been a 15 per cent rise p. a. in claims against doctors for medical negligence', but does not cite a source for this. Requests for clarification produced no new information.

The claim that the incidence in the 1980s was rising was leant weight by the Medical Protection Society (MPS), the smaller of the two English medical defence organisations (MDOs), who revealed that whereas in 1983 about 1,000 claims had been filed with them, in 1987 more than 2,000 claims were filed (MPS, 1989). However, MPS data are complicated by the fact that they include members in Ireland and dentists. In trying to establish the scale of litigation Ham et al were obliged to write to regional health authorities to try and get more information 'in view of the limited information held by the DHSS' (Ham et al, 1988), which then only collected information from health authorities on awards over £100,000. They received detailed replies from the legal advisers of six regions concerning annual claim rates for 1986/87, but this can only give an indication at best of the overall picture (ibid.), and anyway is now rather out of date. In 1985 the Medical Defence Union (MDU) was said to have received about 9,000 cases relating to potential litigation, of which some 600 related to obstetrics and gynaecology, and approximately 80 to brain damage in the infant (Symonds, 1985). The recently set up Clinical Negligence Scheme for Trusts (CNST), which operates in England only, will in due course have data on legal actions which result in damages being awarded, although this is complicated by the level at which hospital Trusts enter the scheme, and so will not be comprehensive. In addition, claims which are successfully repudiated and incur no damages payments may not feature on the CNST assessment of the extent of litigation

Some data on the rapidly increasing subscription rates for the MDOs in the 1980s has been published (Ham et al, 1988), indicating that the cost of litigation, at any rate, was rising. While this rise was halted by the introduction of NHS indemnity for hospital doctors in 1990, it has been resumed, with obstetrics singled out as an especially high risk area (MPS, personal communication). That obstetrics poses a particularly high financial risk has long been known, and is due to the cost of bringing up a handicapped child. A former Chief Medical Officer, Sir Donald Acheson, pointed out in a speech to midwives some of the difficulties of litigation which concerned children with cerebral palsy (Acheson, 1991), and there has been some debate about the relationship between intrapartum events and cerebral palsy.

MPS figures released in the late 1980s acknowledged that while those involved in obstetrics and gynaecology made up three per cent of their membership at that time, they accounted for 29 per cent of claims made, and 36 per cent of the amount paid out in damages (MPS, 1989). While this confirms that the specialty is a very high risk one, it does not tell us how what proportion of these cases were obstetric and what proportion gynaecological; neither does it tell us about the incidence of litigation, since this only applies to cases in which the plaintiff/pursuer is successful; nor does it tell us of the success rate for plaintiffs/pursuers or the scale of the payments.

The number of claims, then, appears to be up, but it cannot be concluded with certainty that the limited available information is representative. Exactly what happens to these claims again is not routinely disclosed. One study took one hundred files at random from 324 medico-legal cases in the West Midlands Health Authority in 1984. After three years, 73 had been withdrawn, 12 settled out of court, one lost in court, and 14 were still pending, 9 of which were thought likely to go to court (Hawkins and Paterson 1987). The high rate of abandonment is very striking, and would seem to confirm the findings of the Pearson Commission of the 1970s (Pearson 1978). Pearson had found that of 500 claims made against doctors, 60 per cent had been abandoned, 34 per cent settled out of court, and five per cent had gone to trial; this represented just 25 cases, and 20 of these were won by the defendants/defenders. This rate of success for the plaintiff/pursuer (between 30 and 40 per cent, which includes those settled out of court) compares with a rate of 86 per cent in other personal injury cases (Fenn and Dingwall, 1989). Such a relatively low success rate puts the reported fears of practitioners concerning litigation into some perspective.

While such reports do not answer comprehensively the essential questions of why and how often people sue, they have provided a basis for further research, including that detailed here. A number of very interesting questions concerning standards of care and training have been raised, and it seemed pertinent to ask those practitioners who might be most involved what they thought about these matters. While the parallel research was examining actual legal files, and has identified the rate of perinatal litigation in Scotland and the two English areas since 1980, this part of the investigation targeted obstetricians and midwives to elicit their views about litigation as well as many of its related features.

CHAPTER TWO

Litigation: How Much and Why

How much litigation?

Some of the claims made about the incidence of litigation have been discussed in Chapter 1, although there has been very little published on the actual incidence of litigation. Some figures concerning cerebral palsy cases have been quoted (Acheson, 1991), but apart from this and a few other small scale studies (Hawkins and Paterson, 1987; Ennis and Vincent, 1990; Hall 1991), there is a dearth of comprehensive data in the literature on this topic. Such media coverage as there is tends to highlight specific cases, often from the point of view of damages awards (Carson, 1988; Anon, 1997a).

Respondents were asked whether they felt there had been a rise in litigation in obstetrics/ midwifery over the last ten years, and, if so, what in their opinion had caused this. Of the 209 obstetricians who answered this question, 189 (90%) agreed, six (3%) disagreed, and fourteen (7%) were unsure. These answers were almost identical to those of midwives (86%, 3% and 10% respectively):

Figure 2.1   Do you feel there has been a rise in litigation in obstetrics / midwifery over the last ten years?

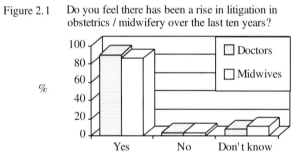

Doctors of all grades were of the opinion that litigation has increased, with the consultants (at 98%) most likely to agree; least likely were the GPs, at 78%. It was interesting to note that all of the English doctors agreed, compared with 90% of the Scottish hospital doctors.

Midwives of all grades were also strongly of the view that litigation has increased (least likely to agree were I grades – 82%; most likely F grades – 88%). There was a similarly limited range of opinion when analysed by size of unit, indicating that wherever midwives work, they feel litigation to be increasing. This may contradict the theory that a 'culture of litigation' is most likely to be found in larger units which have a higher proportion of high risk patients. Looking at the answers by length of experience, the midwives least likely to agree with the question were, not surprisingly, those who have worked for less than three years (76%). Given the lack of published information on the frequency of litigation, these answers may reflect a popular feeling rather than a knowledge of actual figures, or knowledge of people involved. However, this should not detract from the strength of feeling evident in the answers.

Perceived reasons for litigation

Respondents who had answered Yes were asked to suggest why this might be so; the most common answers are shown in the following Tables (many respondents offered more than one explanation).

Table 2.1:
Most commonly cited causes by midwives of a perceived increase in litigation

Most common causes	Cited by (%)	n=
Increased awareness	57.3	1032
Increased expectations	22.4	404
The media	19.7	355
More litigious society	10.7	194
Influence of USA	6.3	114
Deterioration in NHS	3.9	71
Financial gain/Greed	2.8	51
Loss of trust	2	36
The desire or need to blame	1.8	33

Table 2.2:
Most commonly cited causes by doctors of a perceived increase in litigation

Most common causes	Cited by (%)	n=
Increased expectations	49.7	105
Awareness	26.5	56
Media/publicity	18.5	39
General change in the public	18	38
Legal Aid changes	11.8	25
The need for money	4.7	10
Desire/need to blame	4.3	9

Two obstetricians added further comments about how society generally may have changed.

A 'me generation' attitude of wanting compensation for any untoward incident, however trivial.

Greater feeling by the general public that if anything goes wrong someone must be to blame – applies to anything from medical to bad weather, train crashes etc.!

Although increased awareness was the most commonly cited reason among midwives, the notion of increased expectations brought the most additional comments.

I feel people are too quick to criticize medical/midwifery staff if anything goes wrong. They expect us to work under increasing pressure, pay us peanuts and expect unrealistic care...they expect me to be a demi-god capable of doing a hundred and one things at one time with the prospect of being litigated against if I do anything wrong.

I believe that nowadays people's expectations may be too high. If a pregnancy has either an undesired or even a tragic outcome this is viewed as negligence rather than a possibly unavoidable occurrence. There is now a commonly held belief in the UK that one should receive financial recompense for loss or injury irrespective of the circumstances.

If expectations are too high, what may have caused this? Several explanations were offered.

I think midwives, and information available, set women's expectations too high, and they will never realistically reach it. We as a group do not discuss enough in the antenatal period the possibility of the ideal not being met. Therefore we set ourselves up to be sued over numerous scenarios, from psychological trauma to physical trauma.

Obstetricians and paediatricians insinuate that outcome will be 100% – this is impossible to guarantee in childbirth where there is so much we do not know.

Parents' (and grandparents') expectations of a live and healthy baby from every pregnancy are very high in our culture. I feel this is unrealistic, and that the medical profession are partly to blame for fostering this by giving an impression that obstetric technology and intervention has an answer for every problem

The notion of a more litigious society was highlighted by comments about the American influence, lawyers, and the apparent belief that money can be made easily.

I feel that litigation in general has risen in the last few years due to an 'Americanized' attitude of "Sue if you think you can get anything for your trouble" – an attitude which lawyers seem to wish to perpetuate, probably because it's in their own interests.

Awareness about health; rights; law. Potentially a rise in cases in this area due to a firm of lawyers who are representing clients for a proportion of any settlement – no other fees.

In general, litigation is becoming apparent in situations where people are trying to chance their luck in getting a monetary solution.

Unfortunately the few I am aware of in my area are from people from poor but militant backgrounds who see it as a way to make money quickly.

Public awareness and public ignorance to gain money by whatever means possible.

It should be noted that contingency fees, mentioned by one respondent, whereby a solicitor negotiates in advance of accepting a case a percentage of any damages which might be won, are not in fact legal. The Law Society of Scotland fears the potential abuses of such a system (for instance a small firm of local solicitors accepting a percentage for a case, and then 'selling it on' to a larger specialist firm more likely to win, still accepting some of the arranged percentage) and the consequent tide of bad publicity which would ensue. The alleged deep unpopularity of American lawyers is cited as what might be expected were this aspect of US law to be copied here. Speculative fees, on the other hand, a 'no win no fee' arrangement, are legal.

Some clearly felt that an increase in complaints and litigation reflects unfortunate changes in society, as the following comments show.

An attitude of 'Let's complain/sue and see what we can get.'

Demand for the right to perfection in society as a whole without the client accepting any responsibility or the possibility of human error.

Clients who know that they can very often end up with cash in an out of court settlement regardless of the validity of their complaints.

Loss of respect due to poor professional conduct by a minority.

There were many other causes cited, among them the influence of consumer groups, increased technology, poor communication, easier access to notes, inexperienced and unsupported staff, and clinical error. There were several who felt that changes in the health service accounted for a rise in complaints and subsequent litigation.

Incongruence between 'info' given to clients (local and governmental) on services and what is found in reality, e.g. named midwife, staff/client ratios.

Government's 'Patients' Charter' – it has backfired – patients now encouraged to complain.

Patient's Charter – but no Charter to protect staff.

Staff shortages; junior medical staff being left in situations for which they have not been trained.

Some respondents felt recourse to litigation to be understandable, and even a positive aspect of modern health care.

Unwillingness on behalf of medical staff to *apologize* – they're so frightened of legal action if they admit liability that they say nothing ... parents feel that their only way of finding out *what* happened is to go to a solicitor.

I like to look at it in a positive way, i.e. women are more aware of their rights.

I think litigation is on the increase because people are better informed and more assertive than previously, and rightly so.

Parents are no longer intimidated by medical professionals and technology.

On the whole, however, respondents appeared to view litigation with undisguised trepidation; one midwife summed up her reasons for a perceived rise in litigation this way.

Public awareness, cute lawyers and the £ sign.

Given this large number of midwives believing litigation to have increased, did they discuss this at work with their colleagues? 575 (32%) said they had discussed it often, 1,046 (59%) had discussed it once or twice, with only 153 (9%) never having discussed it. Interestingly, 135 (88%) of this last group said they thought there *had* been a rise in litigation, whereas only 85% of those who had discussed the possibility of being sued either once, twice or often thought there had been a rise. By grade, the most likely to have discussed it often were the H grades (57%, or 16 of 28). There was no consistent association between grade and answering 'Often', however, and the H grades were a small group. However there was a clear association between this answer and increasing length of experience, which is perhaps not surprising.

Figure 2.2   Midwives who have often discussed the possibility of being sued (analysed by length of experience)

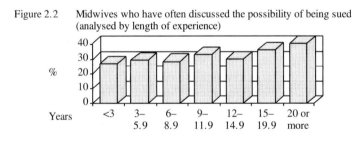

Doctors were also asked whether they had discussed personal involvement in litigation with colleagues (as distinct from discussing the possibility of being sued, which was covered in the following question). 70 (33%) had discussed it often, with a further 102 (49%) having discussed it once or twice. 38 (18%) said they had never discussed it. By grade consultants were by far the most likely to have discussed it often, but it was also striking that the English doctors were far more likely to have discussed it often (57%, compared with 33% of Scottish hospital doctors). The GPs were far less likely to discuss this – 42% said they had never done so. There was, perhaps unsurprisingly, a distinct shift in answers depending on the respondent's length of experience: those who had never discussed it averaged seven years in obstetric practice, those discussing it once or twice had an average of 13 years, and those discussing it often averaged 17 years. Discussing with colleagues the possibility of being sued showed very similar responses, and again the English doctors were far more likely to say they had done this often (62% compared with 38% for the Scottish hospital doctors).

Medical accidents

Respondents were asked whether they believed that the number of medical accidents has risen sharply over the last 10–15 years, since this is a possible explanation for an increase in litigation. Few doctors agreed with this proposition.

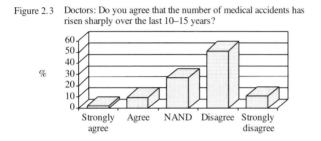

Figure 2.3   Doctors: Do you agree that the number of medical accidents has risen sharply over the last 10–15 years?

Those who agreed or strongly agreed came from almost exactly the same size of unit as those who disagreed/strongly disagreed or who were unsure, and were qualified for only slightly longer (14.6 years compared with 13.4). It was noticeable that a far greater proportion of the English doctors disagreed or strongly disagreed with this notion: 86% compared with 59% of the Scottish doctors. Why this should be so is unclear.

The doctors were then asked whether they felt that financial pressures in the NHS might affect clinical practice to the extent that it becomes less safe; on the face of it this would increase the number of medical accidents. Over half (57%) agreed that this was the case; there was little difference between the grades, but it was noticeable that the GPs (at 63%) were most likely to agree.

Among midwives, slightly more agreed that medical accidents may be on the increase than disagreed (29% compared with 24%), and there was an apparent association between agreeing and increased length of experience. However, almost half (47%) neither agreed nor disagreed, the least experienced being more likely to fall into this category. Since little data are published on this matter, it is really a matter of conjecture. Comments, like the answers, were mixed, with the media again perceived as playing a significant role.

> I don't think there has been a rise in medical accidents in the last ten years, but do think that media coverage jumps at any story given half a chance. People seem more willing to take a grievance to the papers, whose interpretation has often bent the truth.

> I feel there has been a rise, but feel that accidents were covered up in the past.

Medical accidents are not on the increase but those that occur are more widely publicized.

No-fault compensation

As noted in Chapter one, the law of medical negligence is fault-based, but there has been considerable discussion of possible alternatives, and indeed other countries have adopted no-fault schemes. Up and running for many years in Sweden and New Zealand, and more recently in parts of the USA, it has been advocated for obstetrics in Australia (Fisher, 1990), and heralded as a solution to the many problems of the tort/delictual system.

However it is by no means clear how the system would operate in practice. Proposals to copy either the Swedish or New Zealand system have been criticized on the grounds that the New Zealand scheme's original certainties have been eroded (McLean, 1988), and that such a move would be very expensive (Ham et al, 1988). Simanowitz (1987) notes that in Sweden brain damaged babies are not included in the no-fault scheme, and claims that to include them here would make the system unviable. Oliphant (1996) points out that lessons learned from the New Zealand experience may be valuable if a no-fault scheme is to be introduced in Britain, although the Winterton Report, while considering some of the merits of such schemes, preferred to attack litigation on a number of other fronts (House of Commons, 1992).

When the BMA opposed the possibility of a no-fault scheme in the 1970s it claimed that the current fault-based system was one way in which doctors could show professional freedom, it being felt that a state-run system would encroach on the profession's autonomy. That it has changed its mind is evident from its own Working Party report (BMA, 1987) and editorials and leading articles in the British Medical Journal (Smith R, 1988; Dyer, 1990). Proponents of such a scheme have argued that it will simplify the compensation process, and in theory it ought to lessen the delivery room tensions which appear to be commonplace.

The doctors were asked if they would prefer obstetrics to be covered by a no-fault scheme, and were heavily of the opinion that such a scheme would be preferable:

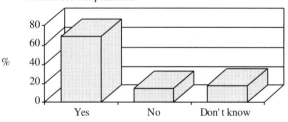

Figure 2.4   Doctors: Would you prefer obstetrics to be covered by a no-fault scheme for compensation?

By grade, the most likely to answer 'Yes' were the Consultants (75%) and the GPs (89%); no GPs answered 'No' to this question. The Scottish hospital doctors were slightly more likely to answer 'Yes' than their English counterparts (68% compared with 62%).

One respondent commented:

> In some ways 'Yes', but fear that inappropriate settlements would be made out of court, even though they should never even reach the court stage.

This is certainly a fear for practitioners, for despite the fact that such payments would be made on a 'no-fault' basis, the implication which many will take is that the care given has been substandard, and perhaps negligent. While this may sometimes be the case, clinicians may be concerned that their name and reputation may suffer irrespective of the particulars of each incident.

Midwifery support for no fault compensation was not canvassed, but several midwives mentioned that they felt this to be a more equitable system for compensating those who have suffered medical mishap. Further discussion of the possibility of a no-fault scheme is given in Chapter 11.

Cerebral palsy

Cerebral palsy has been one of the most publicized features in the current debate about perinatal litigation. In part this is because such cases are newsworthy, both from the point of view of the portrayal of a handicapped child as the victim of a clinical blunder, and because of the amount of damages which may be awarded. These are at the very top of the league of damages payments in medical negligence, mainly because of the cost of providing for a profoundly handicapped child for his or her entire life.

In such legal cases it is usual for the plaintiffs/pursuers to claim that the handicap was caused either by non-recognition by staff of prenatal asphyxia (some would like the term 'fetal distress' to be superseded by 'fetal compromise'), or that, having recognized it, adequate steps were not then taken to deal with the situation – usually by prompt delivery of the child. This being the usual line of approach from the plaintiffs/pursuers, courts have spent much time looking at the question of distress and subsequent asphyxia.

The connection between fetal distress/birth asphyxia dates to the work of Little in the 19th century (Little, 1861), but serious doubt has been expressed in recent years about this apparent connection. Hensleigh et al (1986) criticize the fact that 'Untested, unproved and invalid theories that emerged in the 1950s stimulated the assembly of much data that are at odds with the notion that the pathways of causation for cerebral palsy and perinatal mortality are identical'.

Current research suggests that birth asphyxia/trauma is implicated only in a small minority (8–10%) of cases where cerebral palsy results (Blair and Stanley, 1988), yet many legal actions alleging specific intrapartum causation are brought against obstetricians and midwives. Respondents were asked about the perceived causal relationship between cerebral palsy and birth asphyxia/trauma to see whether practitioners themselves are aware of current thinking in this field, the argument being that if practitioners themselves are not aware, it is unrealistic to expect the lay public to be.

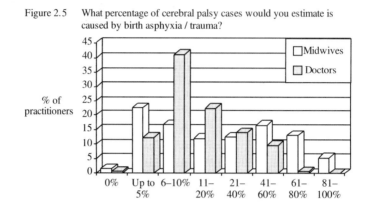

Figure 2.5   What percentage of cerebral palsy cases would you estimate is caused by birth asphyxia / trauma?

By and large the obstetric respondents appeared to know the relevant figures; midwives were much more likely to overestimate the causative influence of birth asphyxia/trauma. It would appear that midwives need to become more aware of the relevant research in this field, given the immense importance of legal actions concerning cerebral palsy.

While 40% of midwives who answered this question correctly estimated the rate as 10% or less, many were clearly unsure (742–41%) did not respond to this question), and some gave huge over-estimates. If one aim of the current research into cerebral palsy is to show how it can only be detected and prevented in a small minority of cases, so reducing the number of hopeful (but hugely expensive and time-consuming) legal cases which are brought under this head of claim, then it seems that many midwives need to be educated about the aetiology of cerebral palsy. This in turn can be passed on to parents, who may otherwise feel that they have a justified and automatic case against practitioners if their child turns out to be handicapped (Bastian, 1990). The need for informed decision making has often been made; disseminating information about this subject could help to resolve misperceptions which otherwise can lead to bruising adversarial legal actions.

Summary

- A large majority of both obstetricians and midwives believe litigation has increased sharply within the last ten years (90% and 86% respectively), despite a lack of comprehensive data in the literature which might confirm this. Few disagreed that litigation had increased, although 7% and 10% respectively stated they weren't sure.

- An increase in awareness and expectations on the part of the general public is believed to be the principal cause of this. Such a strong perception indicates that litigation is much more widely discussed than previously, and clearly it poses a serious potential threat to practitioners. A significantly higher proportion of the English doctors said they had often discussed litigation with colleagues.

- The majority of midwives appeared to be unsure of the incidence of cerebral palsy which can be attributed to birth asphyxia/trauma. Many more doctors were able to cite the currently accepted rate for this causal connection. Given the popularly held view in society that brain damage in an infant is always preventable, midwives need to be aware of these figures and need to take their part in educating the public about this aspect of childbirth.

CHAPTER THREE

Personal Involvement

As with overall figures for litigation, the likelihood – from a statistical point of view – of a practitioner becoming involved in litigation is not generally known. Limited data from the USA is available: Baldwin et al. (1991), looking at individual obstetricians with malpractice experience between 1982 and 1988 (the very years when litigation was supposedly hitting 'crisis' levels), estimated an average of one claim per 3125 deliveries.

Personal involvement: doctors

Personal involvement in perinatal litigation concerning allegations of negligence varied: just over half the obstetricians had never been involved, and even 32% of the consultants were in this category.

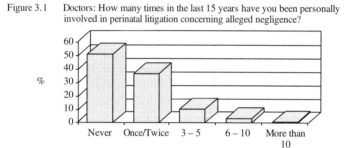

Figure 3.1 Doctors: How many times in the last 15 years have you been personally involved in perinatal litigation concerning alleged negligence?

The likelihood of being personally involved in litigation concerning alleged negligence was again positively associated with increasing length of experience. Those who had either never been involved, or had only been involved once or twice, had an average of twelve years' experience, whereas those involved three or more times had an average of twenty years' experience.[1] With increased experience came more senior status: the consultant grades were involved most often, and almost all of those involved more than three times had at least fifteen years' experience.

This may simply reflect the possibility that the longer an obstetrician's involvement and experience, the more likely they are to have direct experience of litigation. With consultant status there has traditionally been the acceptance of responsibility for the actions or omissions of those working within the consultant's team, as one consultant explained:

---

1 This was extremely significant statistically: p < .00001; calculation by Anova.

(Never personally involved, but) Patients under the care of 'my' team have been involved 6–10 times.

With the development of midwife-only care in certain units, and a significant reduction in the amount of input obstetricians may soon have to the care of many 'low risk' women, this may be about to change. It is possible that the vicarious responsibility of the consultant may be significantly reduced by such moves. However, to confound the theory that increasing length of experience necessarily predisposes to legal involvement, analysis of the length of experience of the consultants was carried out: this was very similar across all answers, as shown in the following Table. Likewise, size of unit appeared to matter little, although there was a weak positive association between legal involvement and increasing number of personal deliveries.

Table 3.1:

Consultants involved in litigation – by length of experience, size of unit, and number of deliveries personally undertaken

Times involved in litigation	No. of consultants	Average length of experience (years)	Average size of unit (deliveries)	Average no. deliveries p.a.
Never	29	22	3360	42
Once or twice	37	19	3768	50
3–5	17	22	3179	53
6–10	7	22	3771	65
More than ten	1	20	4500	150

If length of experience and size of unit do not help to explain a consultant's likelihood of legal involvement, the answer must lie elsewhere. Respondents were not asked the circumstances of their involvement, so it is not known whether the increased involvement in clinical matters - measured by conducting more deliveries - predates and predisposes towards legal involvement, or whether it is a result of such legal involvement, and in fact occurs in an attempt to supervise juniors more closely and help prevent the circumstances in which further legal actions may arise. Unsurprisingly, those of consultant grade were by far the most likely to have acted as an expert witness in legal actions, although the numbers are relatively small: only 30 had done this three or more times within the last five years. If, as most respondents believe, there has been a rise in the incidence of litigation, then there will have been a corresponding rise in the need to seek out expert testimony and comment. Certainly it is this researcher's experience, having read many perinatal legal files, that the same names crop up frequently. There have been moves mooted to establish lists of expert witnesses (or those prepared to write expert opinions) in an attempt to simplify the legal process (Sharp and Chamberlain, 1992), which is not infrequently held up by delays in obtaining expert reports. Those acting as experts in this manner are likely to be senior members of the profession who all have many other commitments, and the legal process – already slow – is made no quicker when awaiting the arrival of a report.

Personal involvement: midwives

Few midwives had been personally involved: only 80 (4.5%) of the whole sample. These respondents were mainly clinically based; length of experience and size of unit varied.

Table 3.2
Midwives involved personally in legal actions relating to alleged negligence

Size of Unit (dels per year)		Grade		Length of experience (years)	
Less than 100	(1)	E	(17)	Less than 3	(1)
100–999	(3)	F	(25)	3 – 5.9	(2)
1000–1999	(2)	G	(35)	6 – 8.9	(5)
2000–2999	(6)	H	(1)	9 – 11.9	(9)
3000–3999	(3)	I	(2)	12 – 14.9	(3)
4000–4999	(4)			15 – 19.9	(5)
5000 or more	(8)			20 or more	(5)
Unspecified	(3)			Unspecified	(2)

Numbers are indicated in brackets.

Of the 80 who said they had been personally involved, 18 came from the English sample, a significant finding in statistical terms.[2] Without knowing more about the circumstances of such involvement it is difficult to know how much emphasis can be put on such a finding, but this does appear to suggest that the direct experience of litigation may be markedly divergent on different sides of the Border. The parallel research into the actual incidence of litigation indicates some interesting cross-border differences.

Of the total sample 44% (n=779) stated they knew of a midwifery colleague who had been involved, and 33% (n=590) knew of a medical colleague. The questionnaire did not ask where such colleagues worked (e.g. in the respondent's current unit or area of work or a previous one), and so analysis by these variables is less enlightening. However those working in units of 2,000 deliveries or more were more likely to know of such a colleague, and the Labour ward in both cases was the most common area of work for the respondent.

There appears to be no automatic correlation between knowing of someone involved in litigation and a belief in a general rise in litigation: 27% of those who said they didn't

---

2 18 from 231 compared to 62 from 1497: p<.01 (analysis by Chi-square)

think litigation had increased (and 32% of those who answered 'Don't Know') *did* know of someone involved in litigation. It would appear that not everyone will generalize about such subjects based on their personal knowledge. There may of course be some overlap in people's minds between litigation (the formal involvement of a solicitor in allegations of negligence) and complaints.

The question specified legal action relating to alleged negligence: a high proportion (87%) said they believed a rise in litigation had occurred, yet only 57% said they knew of anyone involved. It may be that, as with people's attitudes to the crime rate (cf. Hough and Mayhew 1985), many people's fear of litigation is much higher than their actual experience or first hand knowledge.

Some respondents gave accounts of personal involvement in or knowledge of legal cases.

> I am presently working in a unit where we are in the throes of litigation. Information has been 'leaked' to the press causing irreversible damage to our unit. Our clients are distant with little trust. It has affected us all very badly; it will take us years to get rid of this bad press ...

> I have experienced a litigation case ... I was unhappy about aspects of her care, although not the (specified) medical treatment ... at that time I was both inexperienced and also less assertive. Within the unit I work now there is also the opportunity to talk to women in an open and explanatory way. In the previous unit it would have been very difficult to discuss any problems with women, mainly because it was an obstetric led unit ...

> I have been personally and directly involved in litigation. Support from the RCM was very good, as was the support of midwifery colleagues. Obstetricians didn't want to know. This litigation came about as a direct result of a lawyer 'encouraging' a client to sue when there was no real case to be answered. Result: extremely demoralized midwife who had to write report after report; unhappy client who had no real case in the first place.

> I found the period relating to the allegations of negligence to be very stressful. I felt very isolated, even though I had reassurances from the RCM and obstetric and midwifery management that nothing would come of it. Afterwards I wanted to form a support group for midwives who had been in that position. I wanted to be there for them, because I felt no one was there for me.

> I have personally just finished with a litigation case which was settled out of court. Poor attempts from management – no back up or reassurances by anyone except the solicitor who read through statements and reassured me all would be well. It was a very traumatic five years awaiting the outcome.

This feeling of a lack of peer support when something goes wrong was made by several respondents.

> From close experience I have noticed that other members of staff shy away from a staff member involved in litigation. Also doctors tend to cover up mistakes and support each other in it, whereas midwives will report others making mistakes.

> I feel nowadays that you would really be on your own if problems arose, and that your midwifery colleagues would not back you up as they once would have ... It gives me the feeling of working on my own rather than as part of a team.

A more frequently cited comment was the perceived failure on the part of midwifery managers to give support to clinical midwives. This was sometimes accompanied by claims that junior medical staff, by contrast, appear to receive comprehensive support from their seniors.

> Management tend to come down very heavily on midwives and offer little or no support even if the midwife is deemed not to be at fault (shoot first, ask questions later).

> Many fellow midwives feel that in litigation cases midwives are often not given total support from their managers, whereas medical staff appear to 'rally round' and 'stick together'.

> I was involved in a case where a colleague was successfully disciplined ... Being so closely involved has left me very cynical – particularly against management, the medical profession, and very particularly the UKCC!

> There is no support given to the midwives involved, and all too frequently the senior midwives are quick to point the finger of blame and cry out for statements to be written and convey a feeling of guilt. Of the people I have known involved, the senior medical, midwifery and administrative staff behaved like being involved in a witch hunt.

Unfortunately no respondents specifically said they were supervisors, and while it may be assumed that those who gave their grade as 'Manager' enjoy this status, no comments were offered to balance this apparently one-sided depiction.

Summary

- 49% of the obstetricians had been personally involved in litigation at least once, compared with 4.5% of the midwives. The English respondents in both clinical groups were more likely to have been involved.

- Amongst obstetricians increasing length of experience was positively associated with increased involvement in litigation, and consultants were the group most often involved. Amongst those midwives personally involved in litigation there appeared to be no association between this and length of experience, size of unit or area of work.

- Personal experiences of litigation varied. However, many midwives were strongly of the opinion that support from colleagues – especially senior colleagues – in such circumstances was lacking.

CHAPTER FOUR

Perceived Effects

Concern has been expressed that litigation has a detrimental effect on the delivery of health care, partly through its direct effects on staff, and partly through the knock-on effects on the organisation and management of health care. It has been claimed that recruitment to obstetrics in particular has been affected (Pinker, 1991), and that litigation encourages defensive medicine (Simmons, 1990). Others have noted the difficulties in assessing the scale and importance of defensive medicine through conducting self-report studies, claiming that such research tends to introduce bias (Dingwall et al., 1991). Change in practice is multi-factorial, and it is hard to isolate the effect of the fear of litigation on clinical practice.

The Royal College of Obstetricians and Gynaecologists (RCOG) stressed in its evidence to the Winterton Committee (House of Commons, 1992) that recruitment to obstetrics was believed to be under threat because of its image as a litigation-prone specialty. Retention within the specialty is similarly claimed to be difficult (Ranjan, 1993), although Saunders (1992) cites a RCOG study which found that medico-legal problems played a less important role in career choice than expected. However early retirement has apparently become much more attractive for obstetricians (Brahams D, 1991), although how much of this may be due directly to the effects of the fear of litigation is not known. Both the RCOG and RCM have responded to this issue by producing booklets for practitioners (Chamberlain, 1992; Edwards and Mason, 1993).

Clements (1991) points out the difficulty in deciding what constitutes defensive practice: 'I suspect that one man's defensive medicine is another man's risk management'. This illustrates the imprecision of the whole subject, although Ennis et al (1991) claim that 'Our data indicate that tests deemed to be inaccurate are used in clinical practice because some obstetricians fear litigation'. If this is so, then clearly it is a cause for concern: inaccurate tests may lead to a greater level of intervention, causing greater morbidity and personal distress, as well as depleting resources unnecessarily. That the health service has a limited budget is pointed out by Lyall (1988) with reference to the costs of compensation: 'People don't seem to realize that in supporting the drive for compensation they could be spending their own heart attack money'. A finite budget means that resources must be deployed wisely; Bowles and Jones (1989) note that the uncertainties of litigation make budgeting troublesome, a point echoed by Fenn and Dingwall (1995) above in referring to the new insurance scheme for Trusts in England.

Defensive clinical practice

'Defensiveness' in relation to clinical practice is used to descibe the reaction to a threat, whether imagined or real. Black (1990) notes that staff who have been involved in litigation may react by adopting a 'risk avoidance' strategy: 'Doctors may be ... avoiding specialties, procedures, and patients that they perceive carry a high risk of leading to a malpractice claim'. Alternatively, 'defensive medicine' may be seen in terms of risk reduction – i.e. practitioners carrying out more tests and investigations, and intervening sooner, than they would otherwise. An increase in the number of diagnostic tests (such as CTG) and the rate of caesarean sections is seen by some as possible evidence of this (Francome, 1986; Audit Commission, 1997), although the temptation for obstetricians to be influenced by the plaintive 'if only a caesarean had been carried out' is criticized by Roberts (1993). In addition, Dingwall et al (1991) note that the caesarean section rate has increased in countries which have not seen a similar increase in litigation.

The subject of defensive clinical practice is one which is difficult to define, and one which divides practitioners with regard to its merits/demerits and implications for practice. Dingwall et al (1991) point out the difficulties in assessing the scale and importance of defensive medicine through conducting self-report studies, claiming that such research tends to introduce bias. Change in practice, they claim, is multi-factorial, and it is hard to isolate the effect of the fear of litigation on clinical practice (*ibid.* 49).

Respondents were asked whether they had changed their clinical practice at all within the last five years as a result of the fear of possible litigation. Perhaps surprisingly, given such a large majority of both midwives and obstetricians feeling litigation to be on the increase, less than half (45%) of the doctors and only just over half (53%) of the midwives said they had changed their clinical practice. Of the doctors, consultants were the most likely group to say this (56%), but it was very striking that the English doctors were much more likely to say they had done so: 76% compared with 42% of the Scottish doctors. Cross border differences by consultant grade were also noted, with nine out of ten English consultants saying they had done so compared with 43 out of 81 Scottish consultants.

Among midwives there was some association between increasing length of experience and a Yes answer, but this was not absolute; neither was there a consistent association in terms of size of unit:

Figure 4.1   Midwives who changed their clinical practice as a result of the fear of possible litigation (analysed by length of experience)

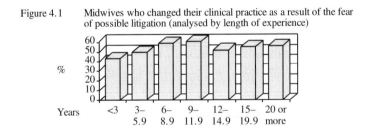

It might have been thought that the larger units, with more high risk patients, would have seen a greater incidence in defensive practice, but this does not appear to be the case. Respondents who said they had changed their practice were asked to state in what way(s) they had done so. The most common answers are shown in Tables 4.1 and 4.2.

Figure 4.2   Midwives who changed their clinical practice as a result of the fear
of possible litigation (analysed by size of unit)

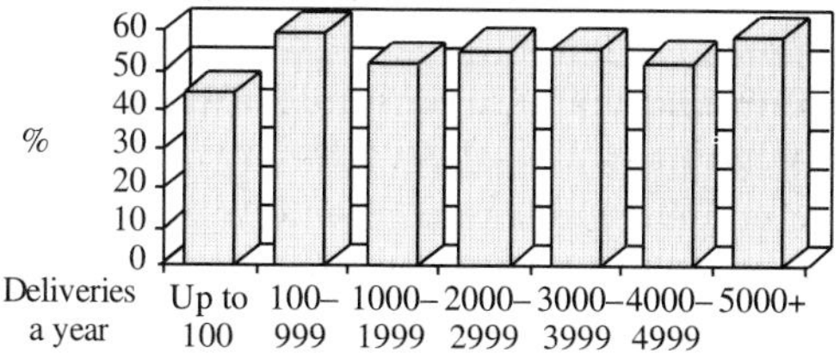

Table 4.1:
*Examples by doctors of a change in clinical practice
due to the fear of possible litigation*

	Cited by (n=)	%
Quicker recourse to caesarean section	36	17.0%
More documentation	20	9.5%
More discussion with patient	10	4.8%
More intervention generally	9	4.3%
More investigations	6	2.8%
Earlier referral to consultant unit (GPs)	6	2.8%
More supervision junior staff	3	1.4%

A growing awareness in the last few years has recognized the increasing incidence of caesarean section, and moves to limit and even reverse this trend have been initiated. It is acknowledged that even by following stricter guidelines for performing caesarean sections, the overall rate for a unit is unlikely to be reduced by more than 1–1.5%. This rate may fall further in years to come as fewer 'repeat sections' are required.

It is disappointing therefore, if entirely understandable, to find that obstetricians still feel that they are being pushed into carrying out caesareans, a finding echoed in the Audit Commission (1997) report. There are certainly many legal cases in which the claim has been made by a pursuer that a caesarean should have been carried out when it wasn't, or should have been carried out sooner than it actually was (personal data; unpublished).

The changes in clinical practice cited by midwives are shown here.

Table 4.2:

*Examples by midwives of a change in clinical practice
due to the fear of possible litigation*

	Cited by (n=)	%
Documentation improved	742	41.5%
Obtain permission for all procedures	136	7.6%
Get medical advice earlier	73	4.0%
Adhere more to unit policies	37	2.0%
Monitor (eg CTG) more often	24	1.3%
Update skills more	19	1.0%
Double check more	14	0.8%

It will be noted that improved documentation is far and away the most commonly cited change in practice. It occurred across all sizes of unit, with those working in the larger units slightly more likely to cite this reason. By area of work, it was noted to be most commonly cited by those in the labour ward (47%) and those working either in a team or a rotational post (45%), and least in those working in a neonatal unit (36%) and on the community (35%). The importance of good documentation is hard to overstate: Cetrulo and Cetrulo's point (1989) that, 'To many, the accuracy and completeness of the medical record reflect the quality of a patient's care. A poor, incomplete, or sloppy record suggests that the care was of a similar quality' highlights this view from a medico-legal standpoint: 'It is difficult, if not impossible, to convince a judge or jury that the care provided was any better than the record' (*Ibid*). Juries, of course, operate in the USA but are practically unknown in medical negligence litigation in Britain.

Analysis by length of experience showed almost a 'bell-shaped' distribution, with those least experienced and most experienced less likely to give this reason than those working for between three and twelve years.

Figure 4.3   Improved documentation as a result of the fear of possible litigation (midwives analysed by length of experience)

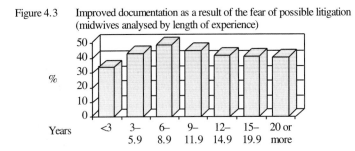

With so many respondents citing this reason, there were many comments added; the following is a small sample.

Because a patient complained about a colleague of mine almost two years after her delivery, especially the midwife's 'decision making', each of us in our unit is now more aware of entering every remark/decision we make in the notes.

We have recently undertaken update in documentation and record keeping which is as a result of increased litigation.

I think the fear of litigation in midwifery is at the back of your mind constantly. In our unit we are very strict in noting lots of information which may appear unimportant at the time, but may be vital if problems arise. This includes writing on the CTG trace when senior midwives or medical staff have observed it.

The time to write up notes is restricted because of lower staff to patient ratios, at a time when accurate and up to the minute note keeping is an imperative due to the litigation threat. As a result the primary objective of patient care suffers.

Some evidently felt the increase in documentation has gone too far.

Ensuring that I write everything down regardless of how trivial it may be.

Document everything, relevant or not.

Improved (in fact almost paranoid) record keeping.

Obtaining permission for all procedures was the second most commonly cited change in practice. This may be viewed as basic good practice, or defensive practice; obtaining permission and getting consent are discussed in Chapter 6. Compared with the claimed improvement in documentation this was not frequently cited, being given by 7.6% of all respondents. However it was noticeable that those who gave this example of a change in practice were much more likely to give the labour ward as their place of work (11% did so).

Other reasons cited included working less (or not at all) in the labour ward – a clearly defensive response; trying to follow research-based practice more often; and challenging medical decisions sooner. The following is a selection of the many comments cited.

Adhering to policy rigidly instead of viewing the individual.

Don't deliver babies anymore.

I no longer deliver in our unit unless well backed up.

I no longer practise midwifery.

Have no qualms in summoning further assistance if I feel there is, or may be, a problem with either mother or baby, no matter how high I may have to go (i.e. consultant).

I did not change from labour ward to community for fear of litigation, but it did cross my mind that you are in a highly vulnerable position in LW (labour ward).

Will use a Sonicaid as well as a Pinards as I feel that my affirming FH is OK may be open to question if parents do not hear the FH themselves.

Swab counts before and after episiotomy repair.

Treat everybody as a potential threat.

Trust clients less and probe circumstances much more than I previously did.

Writing ragged membranes after delivery instead of complete.

Take a 'witness' in difficult situations – re documentation.

I've become independent!

The midwife who now routinely records membranes as 'ragged' rather than 'complete' raises an interesting point. The documentation of the examination of placenta and membranes following delivery has been critical in at least one legal case: the midwife wrote 'appears' before the word 'complete' (which is printed in the labour ward summary of the case notes), and this was held by the plaintiff/pursuer's solicitors to indicate doubt in the midwife's mind that the membranes were in fact complete, although this was challenged by expert opinion. It is not unusual for membranes to be (or to appear) incomplete following delivery, but in such a case greater care must be taken to ensure that subsequent blood loss is not excessive. The use of 'appears complete', or, in the case of this respondent, 'ragged' instead of 'complete', while understandable in terms of trying to cover oneself, may confuse the investigation if a legal action is brought based on allegations of substandard care contributing to haemorrhage.

Obstetricians seem to feel the need for increased documentation rather less, although it can be argued that documentation is not strictly speaking an example of clinical practice. Nevertheless many legal cases have been lost on the basis that documentation was either poor or missing completely, and the need for thorough case records is well made in the literature (Dingwall, 1991; James, 1991).

An improvement in documentation, or increased supervision of junior staff, may be held up as a distinct improvement in standards of care, which reflects the ambiguity with which many view the whole notion of defensive practice. One doctor's defensive medicine is another's good sound clinical practice. One SHO who claimed not to have changed practice added:

But as a trainee I am always keenly aware of potential litigation, and follow advice of my consultants.

Respondents were also asked, irrespective of whether or not they had changed their own practice, whether they felt obstetric clinical practice generally to be becoming defensive. A large majority of the doctors (77%) did so, with only 13% disagreeing, and 10% unsure. GPs, at 53%, were less likely to agree, and there was some difference between the English and the Scottish doctors (Fig. 4.4).

Some comments were added.

The practice of admitting a patient for observation although nothing is obviously wrong, but patient worried, is less prevalent; e.g. decreased fetal movement but CTG OK, or ?SRM but not proven clinically.

Figure 4.4   Obstetric clinical practice generally is becoming defensive

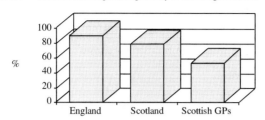

Knowing that any patient might sue leads us to be more aware of what we say and do, and therefore must, at least to some degree, influence our line of management.

I hope not – there is no need to become defensive – just do what one believes is correct and document carefully the reasons, and if necessary the evidence (i.e. studies or audits, etc.)

Doctors who said they had not changed their own practice were even more likely to say that practice is becoming defensive than those who had themselves changed; by the same token, 15% of those who had changed their own practice did not believe clinical practice generally to be becoming defensive.

Nevertheless, a large majority did feel this change to be occurring, and once again the most commonly cited example was more caesarean sections:

Table 4.3:
Doctors' examples of defensive practice

	$n=$	%
More caesarean sections	69	33.0%
More investigations (e.g. scans)	24	11.0%
Quicker intervention	22	10.4%
More use of CTG	14	6.6%
Induction of labour	5	2.4%
More forceps deliveries	3	1.4%
More documentation	3	1.4%

Midwives were slightly less sure that clinical practice is becoming defensive. Of the 1771 who answered this question, 59% agreed, 25% disagreed, and 15% were unsure. By grade there was little difference, except that the managers were much less likely to agree (3 of 8 agreeing, 4 disagreeing). There was some variation when analysing responses by unit size, with those in the smallest units (up to 100 deliveries a year) least likely to agree (53%), and the most likely being those in the next size of unit (100–999 deliveries a year (69%). However it was noticeable that the less experienced midwives (up to six years) were more likely to agree than those qualified for 12 or more years. In this latter group there was an almost exact association between answering yes to both the previous question and this one, whereas this association did not exist for the less experienced midwives (Figure 3.5). It may be surmised that the more experienced midwives are answering the second of these questions based upon their personal experiences, although in fact the association between responses to both questions is not absolute: 53% of those who answered 'No' to the first (i.e. had not changed their own clinical practice) answered 'Yes' to the second (they *did* think clinical practice is becoming defensive), whereas 43% of those who thought clinical practice is not becoming defensive said they had changed their own practice.

Figure 4.5   Change in clinical practice (first column) compared with belief in general defensive clinical practice (second column)

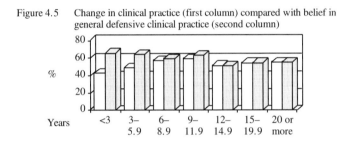

The Scottish-English matched pairs showed more English-based than Scottish-based midwives agreeing that practice is becoming defensive (122 compared with 106; 32 and 49 respectively disagreed). In fact the most commonly cited instances of defensive practice could be argued to be principally or even solely medical features of perinatal care:

Table 4.4:
Midwives' examples of defensive practice

	n =	%
More caesarean sections	352	20.0%
Earlier intervention	210	12.0%
More CTG in normal labour	147	8.0%
More A/N monitoring and investigations	97	5.0%
Induction of labour	68	4.0%
More forceps deliveries	57	3.2%
More fetal blood sampling in labour	55	3.0%
Refer more quickly to medical opinion	52	2.9%
More ultrasound scanning	48	2.7%
More unit policies	18	1.0%

Despite these examples being primarily obstetric in origin, as noted above it was the midwives in the second smallest units who were most likely to agree that clinical practice is becoming defensive. It might be thought that the midwives in the bigger units would be more likely to agree, given these units greater obstetric presence and higher rates of use of obstetric technology. Comments from midwives covered a wide range of matters. One of the most common areas concerned caesarean sections, with many midwives citing 'caesarean section on request'. Another claimed:

LSCS carried out quicker on professional groups more likely to sue (impression only).

The view that a patient's socioeconomic status can affect the way she is treated was asserted very strongly by one midwife.

I do think that if the woman is in the legal profession, or her partner is, it can sometimes affect the way she receives care. I know of one obstetrician who wishes to see such women personally. He also wrote in the antenatal comments section 'Lawyer!' Another senior doctor later added the comment 'So what?', which infuriated the (first) obstetrician, who blamed midwifery staff.

This belief that 'client choice' or pressure will sway the decisions of practitioners was a common theme:

I've seen practitioners intervene sooner than they would otherwise, especially if the couple in question are professionals.

More easily swayed by demands from clients – social induction, social C/S.

Practitioners giving in to demands of the client for invasive tests, rather than using their own clinical skills and judgement.

If women are assertive then they can easily persuade staff to do extra tests.

It is ironic that at a time when some consumer groups are advocating a less interventionist model for maternity care, one perceived effect of the Patient's Charter has been to empower women to demand more tests and operations. Several midwives commented more generally about the way they feel defensive practice is spreading:

The fear of litigation can cause defensive practice – I think this is fairly obvious when we see the present caesarean section rate. Medical colleagues have a fine line to tread in today's climate, but it is sad that some labour ward policies restrict midwives from practising as they would like, and prevent mothers the opportunity of 'carefree' deliveries.

I was involved in litigation; thankfully the case was dropped. It caused me considerable grief, and following this I turned out to be 'defensive' in my practice. My consultant gave me counselling and great support, and I have now reverted back to less defensive means; nonetheless, more wary regarding the situation ...

Doctors and midwives becoming over cautious – e.g. someone complains of a headache – admitted, bloods taken.

Of course what one practitioner views as good safe practice may be viewed by another as defensive, a point which illustrates just how hard it is to measure whether defensive practice really is on the increase.

> As an independent midwife I have been accused of 'practising defensively' by colleagues! This takes the form of making sure I have checked everything thoroughly and that the woman knows about her body and pregnancy, and will inform me if she thinks a problem is arising. All this is documented.

It is not just with obstetricians that this is deemed to be a problem. As the following comments show, defensive practice is encountered by those working in the neonatal area.

> Very often investigations are carried out on a neonate all at one time instead of realistically going through them in the order of most likely given the clinical signs/symptoms. There is a tendency to do all that is mentioned in a textbook.

> More blood tests on babies.

> Routine blood sugar estimations on neonate's weight alone.

Many Community midwives commented on the perceived expansion of defensive practice among their GP colleagues:

> GPs book more patients for consultant unit.

> GPs persuading women to have hospital deliveries.

> GPs reluctant to undertake maternity deliveries they would have been happy to cope with say ten years ago.

> GPs transfer in to consultant unit.

One midwife commented that the increase in 'defensiveness' took some of the enjoyment out of midwifery. Another, who had been personally involved in a legal case said it had made her rethink her career, and that as soon as she could afford it she would leave midwifery.

While defensive practice is difficult to quantify, it does appear to be a concern to a large number of practitioners, particularly in the current climate where a reduction in routine use of technology is being called for by some consumer groups and some practitioners.

An exodus of clinicians?

It has been claimed that the fear of litigation is threatening recruitment to obstetrics, and may even be encouraging practitioners to leave the specialty or retire early from it (Ranjan, 1993), although Blunt (1991) claims that medico-legal problems, contrary to popular opinion, are not a significant deterrent. However, if true, this may have a serious impact on the delivery of health care. In the USA the fear of litigation has been blamed on difficulties in recruiting doctors to obstetrics, which has led to significant shortages of practising obstetricians in some areas, and the need to introduce modified no-fault compensation schemes in West Virginia ad Florida (Symonds, 1992).

Respondents were asked whether they had known anyone to leave obstetrics or midwifery for this reason. Most medical respondents were contacted using work details which may now be a little out of date, so it was possible that some had done this themselves; none, however, had done so. Nevertheless, 37 (17.6%) said they knew of someone else who had either left obstetrics or retired early because of litigation. This may seem rather a high figure, but in fact 25 of these 37 came from just seven different units, and eight respondents came from just two English hospitals, and so it is possible that several respondents were thinking of the same person. Of course with job mobility amongst the junior grades (12 answered that they knew someone who had left) it cannot be assumed that the practitioner who left was based at the respondent's current unit. Nevertheless, there may be some fallout from knowing of a colleague who has left obstetrics because of the fear of litigation; it may be that this promotes discouragement or at least a lack of enthusiasm about the job.

A more accurate measure of disenchantment was asking whether the respondents knew of anyone who had considered leaving (as opposed to actually leaving) because of the fear of litigation. Eleven doctors said they had done so themselves, and a further 57 knew of a colleague who had done so. Six of the eleven who said they had considered it themselves had answered that they had known someone else actually to leave obstetrics, and three of the six said they also knew of a colleague who had considered leaving.

Those who had considered leaving worked in slightly larger units than those who said they had neither considered this themselves, nor knew of anyone else to consider this (3554 compared with 3002 deliveries p.a.), but this was not statistically significant. While it is tempting to speculate on the reasons for practitioners to consider leaving, it would be wrong to do this without more information. Follow up interviews with selected respondents are being carried out. Nevertheless it is worth noting that almost a third of respondents had either considered leaving themselves (5%), or knew of a colleague who had done so (27%); this corresponds closely to the answers given by midwives when asked the same question (respectively 5% and 22%). Levels of disenchantment in perinatal care because of litigation appear to be fairly high.

Ninety-one (5%) of the midwives had considered leaving clinical practice; length of experience did not appear to be a significant factor, with midwives from all the length of experience categories included; this was also the case with size of unit and clinical work place.

Table 4.5:

Midwives who considered leaving midwifery
because of litigation or the fear of litigation

Size of unit		Length of experience	n =	Area of work	
100 deliveries p.a.	(3)	Less than 3 years	(9)	A/N, P/N, clinics	(11)
100–999	(8)	3–5.9	(23)	Community	(16)
1000–1999	(10)	6–8.9	(15)	Labour ward	(25)
2000–2999	(17)	9–11.9	(12)	Neonatal	(8)
3000–3999	(12)	12–14.9	(6)	Team/rotational	(31)
4000–4999	(12)	15–19.9	(11)		
5000 or more	(14)	20 or more	(15)		

With numbers as small as these, percentages are less revealing; little can be drawn from these figures since it is not known what were the circumstances of the respondents concerned when they considered leaving. For the eight who said it was the sole reason, three were qualified between 3 and 5.9 years, the rest all over 20 years; three gave 'Team/Rotational' as their area of work, two said labour ward, and one each said community, neonatal, and wards/clinics. As all of these respondents gave a place of work, it is presumed that none of them had actually given up work. It may be seen from some of the comments already made that several had considered leaving but were in fact still practising.

With such small numbers little can be concluded from them, although follow up interviews with some respondents are underway. Many more respondents (387 – 22%) knew someone else who had considered leaving. Perhaps surprisingly there was little association with the length of experience of those who claimed this, although some increase was evident in the proportion of those working for 15–20 years (29%). Again, only a small minority (12%) claimed that litigation was the sole reason, and without contacting these respondents again it is difficult to know the circumstances underlying the reasons for thinking about leaving. A few comments were added to this question.

> Having worked with neonates for a long time (18 years) I would never return to midwifery for fear of litigation.

> Decided not to become an independent midwife. Not so much the fear of litigation, but because they cannot get indemnity insurance at a reasonable price, which in this litigious climate has made them cease to practice.

Two who said 'No' to considering leaving added:

> But general morale very low as job satisfaction has disappeared and autonomy fast disappearing.

> But many midwives are unhappy, and I am glad not to be starting my career now.

Interprofessional relationships

The former Chief Medical Officer, Sir Donald Acheson, claimed in a speech to midwives that obstetricians were telling him that litigation and the fear of litigation were starting to 'poison interprofessional relationships in the delivery room' (Acheson, 1991). Respondents were asked whether they agreed with this claim.

Responses were mixed, with an almost even number agreeing and disagreeing. Figure 4.6 shows these responses for both doctors and midwives.

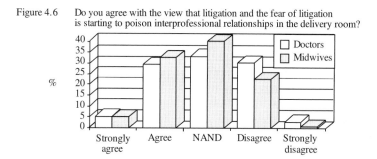

Figure 4.6   Do you agree with the view that litigation and the fear of litigation is starting to poison interprofessional relationships in the delivery room?

One consultant added:

> Disagree on a personal basis, but some midwives have problems with some consultants, and vice versa!

Among midwives the balance is certainly towards agreeing with this statement: 38% compared with 23% disagreeing. By grade, Lecturers and Managers were least likely to agree; most likely were E and F grades (both 40%). More experienced midwives were less inclined to agree, with the 15–20 years group's answers showing a statistical significance when compared with those working for nine years or less[1].

There was no association when analysing this by size of unit, with those in the smallest units as likely to agree as those in the larger units. Perhaps more surprisingly there was almost no difference in the proportion of those agreeing/strongly agreeing when subdivided by place of work. Those who worked in the Labour Ward were barely more likely to agree than those working elsewhere (39% compared with 38% average), and were in fact slightly more likely to disagree with the statement (26% compared with 23% average).

There was some difference of opinion between those working in the Labour Ward, however, but there was no consistent trend in this (Fig 4.7).

Although the numbers strongly agreeing with this were relatively small, there was a statistically significant difference noted in the Scottish-English matched pairs, with 16

---

1 Compared with the 'less than three years group' (p. <.05), and the 3–6 years and 6–9 years groups (p. <.01)

Figure 4.7   Labour ward midwives agreeing / strongly agreeing with Acheson's statement (analysed by length of experience)

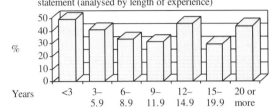

of the Scottish group strongly agreeing, compared to five of the English group. However when 'Agree' and 'Strongly agree' are merged, this difference disappears. The eighty midwives who had been personally involved in litigation were no more likely than those who had not been involved to agree or strongly agree with Acheson. Personal experience, it seems, does not colour such views. Fewer comments were added to this question; some stated that 'poison' was too strong a word to use; one other, agreeing strongly, added '+ +' to indicate the strength of agreement she felt.

Very slightly more midwives agreed with this statement than obstetricians; nevertheless over a third of each group did so, which does not suggest that work relationships are always particularly healthy. It was striking to note that junior and middle grade doctors were more likely to be of this opinion than their senior colleagues; this reflected the midwifery responses, which found that the E and F grade midwives were more likely to agree than their senior colleagues. It might be thought that these staff, who work most often in the actual delivery room, are best placed to comment on such workplace relationships. If this is the case, then such tensions clearly must be addressed.

The image of clinicians

The prevalence of obstetric technology seems to have led some to believe that modern obstetrics has a solution to just about any problem; this impression may be said to have contributed to the high (sometimes too high) level of expectation found in some members of the public. Bastian (1990: 345) claims that '... the profession has, deliberately or not, fostered a consumer perception that, essentially, childbirth can be more or less controlled and babies can be saved if only enough money is spent on the appropriate technology'. This point is echoed by Thomison (1991), and also Ranjan (1993): 'Doctors in general, and obstetricians in particular, are to a large extent responsible for their own downfall', having given the impression that they can achieve more than they actually can.

Respondents were asked whether they felt that obstetric medicine has given this impression. Almost two-thirds (65%) of the doctors thought it was true, with just over a quarter disagreeing. Two doctors who answered 'No' added:

> That may be public perception but hasn't necessarily originated from obstetric medicine.

Public expectations demand this – not the obstetrician.

Seventy-three per cent of the consultants agreed with the idea, which begs the question of who has been responsible for this, and what can be done about it, since it has evidently raised expectations to an unrealistic level for some. This, it will be remembered, was the most commonly cited reason by obstetricians for the perceived increase in litigation in recent years.

Those who had agreed with the proposition were asked to comment on whether the image of obstetricians and midwives had been damaged by this state of affairs. Respondents were clearly of the view that obstetricians at least had been damaged: 71% (96 of the 136 who agreed with the proposition) felt this to be the case; senior grades were more likely to be of this opinion. Midwives were not believed by the obstetricians to have suffered in the same way – just under a third of the 135 obstetricians who answered 'Yes' to the original question felt the image of midwives has also been damaged. One explained that:

Patients always blame medical staff for complications.

Midwives were also of the opinion that obstetric medicine has given the impression that it can achieve more than it actually can: 60% agreed, 24% disagreed, with 16% undecided. H and I grades and Managers were more likely than average to agree; by contrast those midwives with the longest experience (15 or more years) were significantly less likely to agree with this than the more junior midwives. There was no consistent association with size of unit. Two midwives who had disagreed with the question added that it is not obstetricians but the media who have given this impression.

The 1,057 who had said 'Yes' were asked to comment on whether the image of midwives had been damaged by this perception. 58% thought it had, with 28% disagreeing, and 14% not sure. For such a clear majority to feel that midwives are adversely affected would seem to be a worrying issue. One commented:

Public expectations of what medical/midwifery practise can offer is higher than it used to be (Patient's Charter etc.). I don't believe that the general public separates midwifery/obstetric practises – we all work in the same sphere and are therefore all lumped together.

By length of experience, those most likely to agree were those qualified 12–15 years (69%), least likely those qualified less than three years (54%). By size of unit responses differed little from the average except for the two biggest units: 70% of those working in units with 4,000–4,999 deliveries a years agreed, compared to 45% of those in units with a rate of 5,000 or above. Why there should be such a difference is unclear.

Midwives were more likely than doctors to be of the opinion that their own image had suffered. It does appear that a sizeable number of practitioners are of the opinion that their image has been diminished in the eyes of the public, and this must be a matter of concern. How it is addressed remains to be seen: antenatal care, and its whole educative programme for pregnant women, are currently under review (Sikorski et al, 1996;

Tucker et al, 1996). A more realistic programme may help both to educate pregnant women and their families about possible outcomes in maternity care, and to improve the image and status of clinical practitioners.

Signatures may not be enough

Poor standards of documentation have been known to cause lengthy delays in assessing a case which is the subject of a formal complaint or claim. Sometimes the author of an entry in the case notes or kardex is not readily identifiable, and one method of trying to ensure that this is avoided is to require practitioners to print their name. The delay may occur because a critical entry which is signed either illegibly or not at all can lead to difficulty in identifying the staff involved, particularly if there is a long gap between the incident and the date when the complaint or claim is made. In discussing risk management in obstetrics, James (1991) advocates signing all entries in the notes, and printing the author's name for ease of identification.

Twenty-seven per cent of doctors claimed that they always print their name, with a further 37% claiming to do this sometimes; 35% said they never did. Least likely to print names were the GPs (68%). GPs have been known to claim that, with a much slower turnover of staff in general practice compared with hospitals, identification is not a problem. A similar point was made by one senior consultant:

> Don't need to – in the unit everybody knows the signature. Printing is a good idea though.

A far greater proportion of the English doctors claimed always to print their name (57% compared with 25% of the Scottish hospital doctors), which was again reflected in the Scottish-English matched pairs trial of midwives. It would appear that English practitioners have taken this lesson on board much more readily than their Scottish counterparts.

Of the midwives 35% said they always printed their name, 25% said they sometimes did so, and 40% said they never did. No particular association between length of experience or size of unit was noted. One midwife who said she always did commented that to do so was now hospital policy. Another who said she didn't added, 'But current literature now says we should! Must start doing it!' Two comments pointed out perceived difficulties.

> I always sign. Any one can print anything.

> Signature Yes, but not print – some things are too impractical.

Several claimed that there was no need on a personal level, since their handwriting was clear and legible (it took me some time to decipher one of these claims). Another stated that she printed her name at the beginning of a shift, and signed it thereafter when making entries in the notes; an alternative suggestion has been to print one's name on each separate page which is used, following which further entries can be signed. Whether or not either of these becomes mandatory remains to be seen, but it is clear that a relatively simple measure like this could save a lot of time and expense should there be a need to review case notes at a later date.

Summary

- Over half the midwives said they had changed their practice as a result of the fear of possible litigation, the largest single instance being an improvement in documentation. The next most commonly cited reactions were obtaining permission for all procedures, and seeking medical advice more quickly.

- Despite a large majority of obstetricians believing litigation to have increased, less than half said they had changed their clinical practice as a result of the fear of litigation (although many more English doctors had done so). Despite this, a clear majority felt that clinical practice generally is becoming defensive. An increase in the number of caesarean sections was the most commonly cited instance of this.

- Five per cent of each sample said they had considered leaving clinical practice because of litigation or the fear of litigation; a further 27% of obstetricians and 22% of midwives claimed to know of a colleague who had done so. Disenchantment with clinical practice because of the fear of litigation is difficult to quantify, but may be a serious matter if litigation increases sharply.

- Attitudes towards interprofessional relationships in the delivery room among junior grade obstetricians were considerably worse than those of their senior colleagues. This mirrored the midwifery survey, which found that junior midwives, like the SHOs, are more concerned about the detrimental effects of litigation on staff relationships. No fault compensation is favoured by a large majority of obstetricians.

Part II
The Normality of Pregnancy

CHAPTER FIVE

Midwifery Autonomy

The normality of pregnancy and labour

The question of normality in this regard is related to aspects of choice and control. These are critical in modern health care, with an increasing emphasis on the rights of the patient. Maternity care in particular has seen some of the most intense debate on this subject (DoH, 1993a,b), with a growing body of opinion demanding minimal obstetric intervention (Tew, 1986).

Beech (1989) claims that 'when obstetricians took over the care of all pregnant women they brought with them their anxieties and lack of understanding of the normality of childbirth.' Such a view is sometimes presented as claiming that 'no pregnancy or birth is normal except in retrospect', an approach described by the Winterton Report as 'an impediment to the delivery of a style and pattern of maternity care that will meet the expressed wishes of the majority of women who use these services' (House of Commons, 1992).

However it has been claimed that this approach to antenatal care has typified the provision of centralized high surveillance maternity care over the last thirty years or so. Practitioners, the argument runs, aware that Britain was falling behind other countries in terms of infant mortality, and mindful of the potential disasters associated with childbirth, advocated a high degree of supervision and investigation during pregnancy and especially labour. However, the assumption that interventions mean safer childbirth has been criticized (Tew, 1985; 1986).

Nevertheless, Beazley (1995) describes labour as 'an intensive care situation', and claims that 'on admission to hospital patients in suspected labour should be treated as though, at some time during the next 12 hours, a Caesarean section will be necessary' (*ibid*. 296). He further states 'Normal labour can be diagnosed with confidence only in retrospect', the qualifying 'with confidence' being added after the 1986 edition (*ibid*: 295). He is not alone in this view: Chamberlain (1995) in a standard text claims 'No labour can be said to be normal until the third stage is safely concluded ... Labour is best managed by intensive care techniques.' From the answers in this survey, it would appear that most obstetricians agree with this view, although midwives were much more evenly split – in fact slightly more disagreed than agreed.

Little variation was noted when answers were analysed by grade or size of unit; however those midwives qualified the longest (more than 20 years) were more likely to agree or strongly agree (44%) than those qualified less than six years (31%). It is possible that this reflects a trend away from interventionism (or a perceived need to intervene) in maternity care. Whether this will be accepted by obstetricians was questioned by one midwife.

Figure 5.1   Do you agree with the statement that 'No pregnancy or birth is normal except in retrospect'?

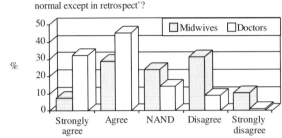

With the increasing numbers of clients prepared to attempt litigation midwives may well find it harder to maintain their areas of medical-free practice. Some obstetricians are willing to quote the 'Pregnancy is only normal in retrospect' cliché to justify their intervention in normal pregnancy and labour in order to exert a degree of control over their clients and the outcome of the pregnancy.

GPs were slightly less likely to agree with this statement, but the view was more popular amongst Scottish hospital doctors: 80% compared with 55% of the English doctors. This perspective may be taken as an indicator of how cautious (and possibly interventionist) a practitioner may be. It can be argued that someone who agrees with the statement is likely to focus on potential pitfalls rather than on the fact that the vast majority of pregnancies are concluded without serious mishap in terms of outcome. The Scottish doctors being more likely to agree perhaps helps explain the apparently lower level of trust given to midwives looking after low risk pregnant women (discussed next).

Midwives' responsibilities

There is a debate about whether obstetricians ought to see women whose pregnancies are uncomplicated (Walker, 1995; James, 1995), with some claiming that the midwife is the practitioner best placed to deal with such pregnancies (Thomson, 1991). The Winterton Report noted that evidence to the committee revealed 'a clear indication of the potential for a damaging demarcation dispute between the professional groups over how labour should be supervised' (House of Commons, 1992).

Whether the desire among obstetricians to ensure a good clinical outcome derives from a paternalistic desire to maintain control, or from a fear that each woman is a 'potential litigant' (Bastian, 1990), is a matter for debate. The view that a good clinical outcome (a healthy mother and baby) is the only criterion for evaluating the success of a pregnancy is one criticized by Beech (1986), who takes the view that maternal morbidity (both emotional and physical) in particular has been a problem invisible to most obstetricians. If the problem is largely invisible, then the dissatisfaction expressed by mothers may be unintelligible to the clinicians involved, yet this may be a factor in deciding to sue.

Respondents were asked whether midwives within their unit are given full responsibility when managing the labour of a woman deemed to be low risk. This question relates to the likelihood of intervention in a woman's labour, and such an issue can affect her perception of the labour's outcome. A number of complaints about inappropriate or mishandled intervention have subsequently become legal claims, and practitioners must be wary of upsetting patients at such a time. This matter also relates to the confidence obstetricians have in the midwives who work in their units.

Overall 34% of the doctors claimed that midwives are always given such responsibility, and a further 56% said this usually happens. There was little difference in responses between the different grades, with those who answered 'Rarely' or 'Never' working in units of at least 2,500 deliveries a year. However there was a large difference between the doctors based in England and those based in Scotland (Fig. 5.2).:

Figure 5.2   Doctors: Are midwives in your unit given full responsibility when managing the labour of a woman deemed to be low risk?

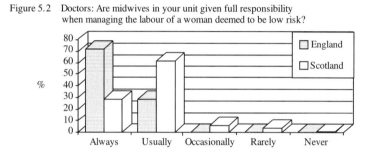

This large difference was also found in the Scottish-English midwifery matched pairs trial. The rate of answering 'Always' was almost twice as high in the English sub-sample: 122 compared with 66, which may say much about the contrasting roles of Scottish and English midwives. Why there should be such a marked difference in the perceived role and responsibility of the midwife on either side of the border is unclear. Mention in the midwifery survey was made of 'the Scottish medical establishment', and the particular role of Scottish obstetricians in the development of maternity care within Scotland. Staffing levels may have something to do with this too. One senior registrar who said that midwives are rarely given full responsibility claimed that it is:

Because they (midwives) involve doctors in almost every case!

One GP who said that midwives are never given full responsibility explained why this is so in a GP-run unit:

Otherwise our involvement and skills would atrophy completely.

It may be that the distinction between 'Always' and 'Usually' is not that great; but why midwives should not always be allowed full responsibility for the normal low risk pregnant woman, in consultant units at least, can perhaps only be explained by further investigation.

Midwife-run units

There are moves towards reclaiming autonomy among midwives, and one area which has been developed in recent years has been the idea of midwife-run units [MRUs] (Henderson, 1993), a move supported in the Winterton Report (House of Commons, 1992). These look after women deemed to be 'low risk', giving them all care and only referring to an obstetrician when a significant problem is encountered. There are possible legal consequences in such moves, for if a clinical outcome is poor, doubts may be raised about whether the patient concerned ought to have delivered in an MRU, or whether the screening for 'at risk' was sufficient. Increased autonomy for midwives carries with it implications for accountability.

Those midwives not already working in an MRU were asked whether they would be happy to do so, taking full responsibility, along with their team colleagues, for a woman's care. Of the 1,522 who answered this, 1,149 (76%) stated they would happily do so, and 372 (24%) said they would not. A ratio of 3:1 in favour of such a move may help the impetus towards setting up such units.

There was little difference of opinion according to length of experience, but the least likely to say 'Yes' were the most experienced: 73% of those working for 20 years or more. The least experienced (less than three years) were keener (75%), and those working 12–14.9 years most keen (81%). By size of unit there was a similar range of opinion, with those working in units with an annual delivery rate of 100–999 most likely to say 'Yes' (83%); those working in units of 2,000–2,999 deliveries a year were least likely (71%). This is still a large majority in favour of working in such a unit, however. The most common reasons given for saying 'Yes' and 'No' to this question are shown in Table 5.1.

Table 5.1:

Would you happily work in a midwife-run unit, taking full responsibility (in conjunction with your colleagues) for a woman's care?

Yes		No	
'This is what midwives are trained for'	634	Prefer consultant cover/full facilities	103
Work satisfaction	101		
Know when to refer	62	Not enough experience	87
Less medical interference	48	Lack of confidence	35
Providing women are low risk	47	Fear of complications	26
Continuity of care	44	Fear of litigation	25
Choice/satisfaction for women	42		
More autonomy	38		

The first reason cited under 'Yes' is a paraphrase. Typical examples were: 'We are fully trained – why not?', 'I am a practitioner in my own right – I know right from wrong', 'That is what midwives are trained to do', 'That's what midwifery is all about', 'Because I am an autonomous practitioner', 'I want to be a midwife'.

There were many comments relating to this topic, some adding a note of caution.

> I strongly believe that these units are an excellent means by which midwives (particularly junior ones) can develop their true midwifery skills and practice – working in an obstetric or consultant unit should be seen as a different type of practice altogether. Many of today's midwives do not seem to know the difference, or care for that matter.

> There is now a great opportunity for midwives to regain care of women previously lost to obstetricians by taking full responsibility for their practice and professional obligations. Sadly not all midwives are thus motivated, and the current trends in devaluing, demoralising and disempowering midwives within the NHS will not encourage the majority of professionals to assert their role.

On the whole, midwives appeared happy with such an idea, providing certain requirements were met.

> Challenging and exciting prospect, also more rewarding. It would require careful supervision, a good educational input, and a high level of midwifery support.

> As long as the midwifery unit is attached to a consultant unit with medical staff available only if invited into the unit.

> If the criteria for risk was clear and there was good back up for emergencies.

Several indicated that they would like to in theory, but needed either to update clinical skills or to gain more experience or confidence before accepting this challenge.

> At this point in my career I am too inexperienced. I am not completely comfortable but I can cope at my own level at present and as I gain experience my level of responsibility will increase hopefully with me.

> I would like to be 'weaned' from a consultant unit to a midwife-run unit.

> I would need to return to hospital to 'brush up' my skills, then would be happy.

Some commented on the need to be able to trust their midwifery colleagues in such a unit.

> Don't know colleagues well enough to know competence of some.

> Prepared to take responsibility for my *own* mistakes.

> Unfortunately we are not supportive enough of one another to make an effort like this really work.

Not all were happy, though, often through being used to the environment of a consultant unit.

> After all my years as a practitioner in a hospital environment, I'm used to all 'mod cons' instantly available.

> Habit – I've worked in a consultant unit so long.

> I am too frightened of litigation. The consultant unit is a safety net.

> I like to have doctors to refer to.

Some respondents cited other obstacles to working in such a unit.

> Salary does not reflect the expertise/skill/responsibility it entails.

> I work in a neonatal unit

> I am a nurse/midwife, NOT a doctor; certain things I have not been trained to do, and have no wish to do anyway. Too much responsibility.

> Too old.

> We already have 'low risk' patients but the obstetricians practice defensive obstetrics and feel *they* are at risk when this is practised and are slowly withdrawing these patients.

Some may consider it a political point as to whether obstetricians will be happy to concede this much 'territory' to midwife-run units. An audit of such a unit claimed that midwife managed intrapartum care for low risk women resulted in more mobility and less intervention (Hundley et al, 1994), but brought criticism from a number of obstetricians (Somerset and O'Donnell, 1995; Smith L, 1995; Jones, 1995; Brocklehurst et al, 1995). It is arguable that with thoughtful siting of such units, the advantages of nearby obstetric backup can be enjoyed without the disadvantages of automatic obstetric surveillance (for instance that more monitoring leads to more intervention and consequent morbidity, without improving the outcome). This has been attempted in midwife-run units in Glasgow, Aberdeen, and London (Hundley et al, 1994; Taylor, 1994; Turnbull et al, 1995).

Given these stated objections to working in a midwife-run unit, were those who currently work in such units completely comfortable with the increased level of responsibility and accountability which this entails? This question was prefaced: 'For midwives already working in a midwife-run unit', and was answered by 183 respondents. I gave no definition of such a unit, and there may be some disagreement as to exactly what constitutes an MRU, since two respondents who gave their grade as 'lecturer' answered this question, one giving her place of work as a consultant unit, the other as a combination. Another 27 indicated on the front of the form that they worked only in a consultant unit. A further 26 worked on the Community, 28 in a GP unit, 60 only in an MRU, and 42 indicated a combination of work places.

Of those who answered it, 160 (87%) said they were happy, with only 20 (11%) saying they weren't; three (1.6%) ticked the box marked 'Other'. With such a large majority comfortable with working in such a unit, the prospects for the development of MRUs appear good. There was some discrepancy in terms of length of experience, but since there are smaller numbers involved in this answer, caution must be taken when interpreting differences. Those working for less than three years were less likely to be happy (78% compared with an average of 87%), as were those with 15–20 years' experience (68%). (Table 5.2)

Table 5.2:

Midwives working in an MRU who said they were completely comfortable with the increased level of responsibility/accountability their job entails

Length of experience (years)	n =	%
Less than 3	18	78
3–5.9	34	94
6–8.9	26	93
9–11.9	27	87
12–14.9	10	83
15–19.9	13	68
20 or more	30	97

The confidence enjoyed by some of these midwives was very striking.

In some ways total control and accountability can be less stressful. No one else to blame except yourself. If your standards are very high you have nothing to fear.

Yes, because there are well defined criteria for care/policies/procedures.

Our Midwife Managed Unit is in close proximity to the (consultant unit) labour ward. Women are transferred there if complications arise, and medical assistance is available at all times if required.

However, this was not universal. Some respondents highlighted problems encountered.

Pressure of work could lead to mistakes and therefore being sued. The unit is extremely busy.

Sometimes the staffing levels are poor in the midwives' unit – it often fares second best due to demands in the high tech unit.

[Our MRU] is heavily dominated by medical staff. As a midwife I feel frustrated by the way medics dictate to us, and they consider the MRU as being tolerated and have a resentful attitude if we refer a case to them. I have worked in London and in Europe as a midwife, and in London midwives have a much higher status and extended role. I think Scotland's medical establishment does not recognize the potential of midwives and therefore we as a profession do not stand up against this due to fear of confrontation, and increasingly litigation.

Management not always supportive; registrars with little experience keen to attack midwifery practice.

Dimond (1994) stresses the need to organize such units so that inter-professional rivalry is avoided, and to have clear guidelines as to the suitability of those who elect to deliver there. Despite the caveats expressed by some respondents, the overwhelming response to this question was that midwives not working in a MRU would happily work in one, and those already working in one are comfortable with the responsibility and accountability involved.

Summary

- Scottish obstetricians were much less likely to say that midwives in their unit are given full responsibility when looking after low risk patients (this view was echoed by the Scottish midwives). It is possible that increased interventions will result from this practice, and this may lead to lowered satisfaction levels in patients. Whether or not patients are predisposed to take legal advice in such circumstances is debatable, but the incidence of complaints about care, especially during labour, have almost certainly increased sharply.

- Three-quarters of midwives based in consultant units said they would happily work in a midwife-run unit, accepting full responsibility (along with colleagues) for the care of low-risk pregnant women. For those midwives already working in such a unit, 87% claimed to be comfortable with the increased level of responsibility and accountability.

CHAPTER SIX

Patient Autonomy

Routine procedures

The scope for autonomy for the pregnant/labouring woman has been discussed at length in recent years (Dimond, 1993; Mander, 1993). This is closely related to notions of choice and informed consent (Beech, 1986). It may be questioned whether the organizational requirements of the health service can allow for a significant degree of flexibility when dealing with individuals, and some might view with suspicion the allegedly recent rapid growth of unit protocols and policies. These aim to ensure that a certain level of care is given regardless of the preference of the individual practitioner, or, it may be argued, the expressed wishes of the patient. Whether such routine procedures constitute an attack on the autonomy of the patient was addressed: respondents were asked whether they had had a woman refuse a routine policy, and if so, to state which one(s).

Seventy-six per cent of doctors said that this had occurred (compared with 64% of midwives), with 19% claiming it hadn't. The more senior obstetricians were more likely to say 'Yes', and correspondingly the more junior more likely to say 'No'.

The most commonly cited examples of a refusal are shown in Table 6.1.

Figure 6.1   Obstetricians who had not had a woman refuse a procedure which was standard policy (analysed by length of experience)

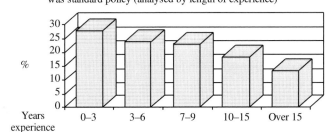

49

Table 6.1:
Examples by doctors of a refusal of a standard procedure

	(n =)
Caesarean section	37
CTG	19
Artificial rupture of membranes	18
Administration of Syntometrine	14
Induction of labour	13
Venepuncture	12
Use of Syntocinon	10

There were other answers too, including forceps delivery, amniocentesis, perineal repair, ultrasound scanning, and vaginal examination.

Nine midwives, from six different units, claimed that in their unit there is no such thing as a routine policy, all care being tailored individually to meet each woman's needs. This claim implies that there are no policies or protocols in place in such units, for however much care is tailored to each individual woman, these must be seen as prescribing routine standard care. Courts may look to such protocols when determining what a reasonably competent practitioner could have been expected to do or to know when deliberating on allegations of negligence (Dimond, 1994). The majority of respondents (64%) did, however, admit to having had routine policies refused (or declined) by women in their care. Length of experience appeared to affect responses only minimally (range 61–65% by group). Analysis by size of unit showed no significant differences either, but those midwives from the smallest units (up to 100 deliveries a year) were least likely (at 51%) to say they had had a refusal of this nature. Beyond this there was no association between size of unit and answer.

The most commonly cited examples of refusal are shown in Table 6.2.

Many others were cited, including admission to hospital, caesarean section, resuscitation of a baby, the daily postnatal check, blood transfusion, medication, and signing consent forms. An interesting note was made by several respondents, namely that some procedures which may be considered arcane or even barbaric today were once standard: it is not so long ago that routine shaves and enemas (cited by 9 and 8 respondents respectively) were given in many units upon admission in labour, and several midwives noted that they had agreed wholeheartedly with the woman's refusal to undergo such procedures. No doctors gave examples of refusal which they said they supported. At the other end of the spectrum several midwives stated that they had had women refuse auscultation of the fetal heart, even when using a Pinards stethoscope. Abdominal palpation and recording of the blood pressure were also cited by several midwives.

Table 6.2:

Examples by midwives of a refusal of a standard procedure

	(n =)
Cardiotocography (CTG)	328
Administration of Syntometrine	262
Venepuncture	218
Artificial rupture of membranes	173
Administration of vitamin K	167
Ultrasound scan	128
Induction of labour	89
Vaginal examination	88
Perineal repair	56
Episiotomy	48

Many of the examples given related more to clinical advice in a given situation being refused: CTG monitoring is much less a routine procedure today (it is claimed), but may be indicated in certain situations; this is discussed in Chapter 8. A refusal in such a situation (many were offered as examples, including the presence of fetal distress – with or without meconium staining of the liquor; a previous caesarean section scar or other known poor obstetric history; induction of labour; use of syntocinon) raises the question of a woman's autonomy, and the rights (if any) of the unborn child. Such situations are subjective, and often complex; detailing them in abstract form will miss the subtleties of the individual situation. Several respondents commented very strongly on this topic.

> There should be forms for clients to fill stating that they have refused the advice of the given midwife and that they are taking full responsibility for their actions.

> I do feel patients should be fully informed and consented for any procedure. However I do feel frustrated when in extreme cases, e.g. fetal distress, that the fetus has no rights.

> Over the last few years I have been involved with women and their partners who consistently refuse sound, reasonable midwifery advice ... There is legislation protecting the rights of women in childbirth; why is there none to protect the midwife?

> Take the case of a woman having her third baby. The last two were delivered by caesarean section for cephalo-pelvic disproportion. She opts for home confinement despite midwifery advice and alternatives being offered to her. When labour commences a midwife is in attendance; there is no progress over three days! Despite the Supervisor being informed on a regular basis, there is no way the midwife is allowed

to leave this woman. Who is supporting her? At one point the midwife is dismissed by the woman, only to be summoned several hours later. What is there to allow the midwife to stand up and say to this woman 'enough is enough'? Nothing! She must remain and continue to give support and take abuse for things going wrong!

I support women's choice, but let's be more for professional sound advice in cases like this. Why should any baby be compromised?

Clearly felt by many respondents was the tension between being the woman's advocate, offering her professional advice, and acceding to her wishes. A common perception appeared to be that the Patient's Charter has given women the right to request or demand certain forms of treatment or care. Opinion differed on how to deal with this.

I think there is a very fine line to be drawn between weighing up the woman's wishes versus intervention, and we must always err on the cautious side and the rights of the unborn child.

Midwives are expected to do so much more because the woman wants it. When I go to my dentist I don't tell him how to take out my teeth(!) but all too often we are told how to do our job.

Surely it is our duty if we work as practising midwives to provide what women want. Plumbers don't say they cannot replumb a bathroom in case there are leaks – surely it is no different.

These last two points illustrate the tension between a 'service provider' and being a professional who prescribes care, again relating to the questions of autonomy and control. Providing choice is a common theme, but it is unclear where the line is drawn between acceding to requests and stressing an alternative viewpoint based on clinical expertise or the requirements of local protocols.

There is an area which directly affects midwifery practice, and that is demands made by women which go against unit policies and increasing demands for alternative deliveries etc. My main fear is that midwives feel a need to meet women's demands or have a professional duty to do so, but are also acutely aware now of possible repercussions – an example that springs to mind is the recent waterbirth at home which caused problems in Hertfordshire.

Clients are given too much information nowadays and this can cause problems as sometimes they do not really understand the full picture resulting in them demanding sometimes inappropriate care which could result in a tragedy … It is a case of 'a little knowledge is a dangerous thing', and certain clients seem to feel that by reading several medical books they know more than the midwives, doctors etc. They also feel they have a 'right' to demand a certain type of birth even though through developing risk factors this is not possible …

One summed up the ideal.

I feel proper antenatal education and discussion, and also giving the client an informed choice, decreases the likelihood of the client objecting to various procedures.

With moves towards more individualized care, despite the continuing presence (and some would say growth) of unit policies, it might be thought that a woman's refusal of a procedure would constitute the last word on the subject, provided that her decision-making has been informed. It is possible that overriding such a decision, if it involved physical contact in some way, might be construed as a trespass (Dimond, 1994). The previous question showed that refusals of procedures or treatments are fairly commonplace; the claim made by Beech (1984) in a stern critique of hospital care, that, such refusals notwithstanding, 'routine hospital treatments [are] given often in opposition to the stated views of patients', was put to respondents. It may be argued that significant improvements in the planning and delivery of such care over the past ten years have changed the picture somewhat; it was certainly the opinion of a large majority of doctors (88%) and midwives (81%) that Beech's view is wrong. While only five doctors (two registrars, two SHOs, and a GP) agreed with Beech, rather more midwives (186) did so. Their level of experience varied, as shown in Figure 6.2.

Figure 6.2   Midwives who agreed that 'Routine treatments are given often in opposition to the stated views of patients' (analysed by length of experience)

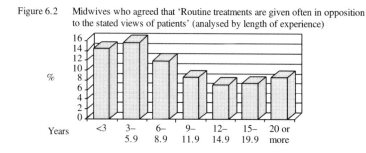

Although the overall numbers agreeing with Beech are small, it is interesting that it is the most junior midwives who are most likely to agree.

This led on to the claim, also made by Beech (1986), that women are accused of putting their babies at risk by refusing routine interventions. I did not specify what sort of interventions, because these are not specified in the original article, and given that almost all respondents answered, it seems that they acknowledged the thrust of the question. Doctors were far more likely to agree with the claim made by Beech than midwives, as shown in Fig. 6.3.

Figure 6.3   Do you agree with the view that women may be putting their babies at risk by refusing routine interventions?

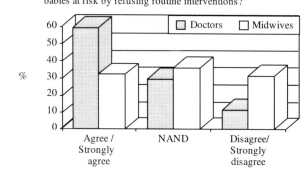

One doctor who neither agreed nor disagreed added:

Whether they are putting their babies at risk or not, choice is theirs, not ours.

It was interesting to note that the English doctors were considerably more likely to agree than their Scottish counterparts (81% compared with 58%).

Insistence

This section echoes some of the issues concerning midwives' responsibilities, which were discussed in the previous chapter. Control and informed choice are sensitive areas in maternity care (Mander, 1993; Jones and Smith, 1996).

Respondents were asked whether, in a situation where a woman in labour had indicated that she definitely did not want to have electronic fetal monitoring (EFM), there were any circumstances in which the respondent would insist upon carrying out this procedure. The reason for asking this question stemmed from a claim made by the solicitors acting on behalf of a plaintiff/pursuer in an action involving alleged negligence. The patient had requested minimal monitoring, and in fact, due to discomfort and at her request, CTG monitoring had been discontinued. Her solicitors stated in a letter:

'Continuous fetal monitoring when the decision was made to give a syntocinon infusion should have been insisted upon ...'

The solicitors appear to be presuming to know the circumstances in which particular forms of monitoring are indicated, and the circumstances in which a woman's stated preferences should be ignored. With a 'retrospectoscope', which gives perfect vision in hindsight, such claims may be made with a feeling of justification. Of course this is not the situation in which practitioners looking after a labouring woman will find themselves. That said, the notions of autonomy and control are – from these responses – not matters which can be said to have been resolved by practitioners as a whole.

Figure 6.4   If a woman indicated that she did not want to have EFM during her labour, are there any circumstances in which you would insist?

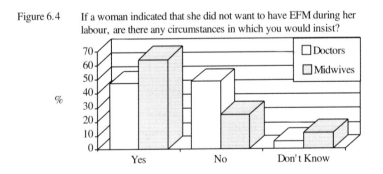

For such a clear majority of midwives to favour this course of action may cause some concern to user groups and patients alike; the much vaunted autonomy of the pregnant woman appears very shaky when viewed against this finding. Concern may also stem from the feeling that a woman's care during her pregnancy or labour could differ significantly depending on which midwife is allocated to look after her.

There were some striking differences when analysing the 'Yes' answers by grade.

Figure 6.5   Proportion of doctors (by grade) who would insist on EFM under certain circumstances

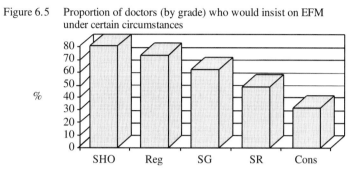

A very similar pattern was noted in the midwives' responses (Fig. 6.6).

Figure 6.6   Proportion of midwives (by grade) who would insist on EFM under certain circumstances

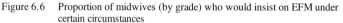
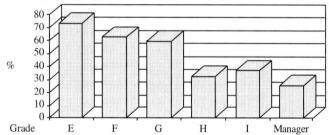

This seemingly stark association between a midwife's job grade and likelihood of insisting on EFM is not wholly to be explained by her length of experience (Fig. 6.7), indicating that while increasing experience may lessen slightly the likelihood, the role actually carried out by the midwife (as indicated by her grade) seems to be more important. The more junior grades may argue that grades H and above are unlikely to spend much time looking after women in labour, and so the question for them may be more theoretical.

Figure 6.7   Proportion of midwives who would insist on EFM under certain circumstances (analysed by length of experience)

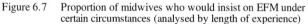
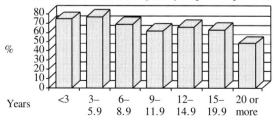

For the junior staff to be more likely to say they would insist may reflect a lack of confidence in other methods of assessing fetal well being (such as intermittent auscultation), and perhaps too high a level of confidence in the accuracy and reliability of CTG machines.

Those who said they would insist were asked to state under which circumstances.

Table 6.3:
Most commonly cited reasons for insisting on EFM

Doctors	n =	%	Midwives	n =	%
Meconium staining	36	17	"Fetal distress"	623	35
Any high risk	26	12	Meconium staining	552	31
IUGR	25	12	APH	192	11
Fetal distress	23	11	IUGR	176	10
APH/IPH	18	8.5	Syntocinon infusion	165	9
Previous caesarean	12	5.7	Prematurity	135	7.5
PIH	8	3.8	PIH/PET	130	7.3
Syntocinon	8	3.8	Poor obstetric history/previous section	108	6
Twins	8	3.8	Twins	74	4
Diabetes	4	1.9	Epidural	64	3.6
			Induction of labour	49	2.7

This situation raises questions of autonomy and control, with one obstetric respondent stating that it was not her right to insist upon any such procedure; several midwives pointed out that doing so could be construed as an assault. Clinicians encountering a patient who has defined pregnancy risk factors but who insists on minimal monitoring and intervention face a difficult decision in determining an appropriate level of technological monitoring. The fear of litigation is used as a reason for insisting on such monitoring, but in fact those respondents who had been most involved in litigation were slightly less likely to say they would insist on it. Of course it is not known what were the circumstances of their legal involvement; the question of intrapartum monitoring may not have arisen, but it certainly is an issue which has been raised in many legal actions.

Other fairly common reasons included breech presentation, prolonged labour, and following the administration of analgesia; less common were maternal diabetes, obesity, reduced fetal movements, and post maturity.

It was disappointing to read comments like:

All patients within the unit have continuous monitoring.

Hospital policy of continuous monitoring.

Mostly because medical staff would dance up and down if we didn't.

Our unit has just accepted routine CTG monitoring on all women.

We have a criteria set by the obstetricians and dare not deviate from this.

Several pointed out how they would hope to avoid such a situation arising.

I would hope that my relationship with the woman would be such that I would never need to insist. That she would trust my judgement.

I do not believe it is in my power to insist – only to ensure the woman is making an informed choice, and I must support her wishes and plan her care appropriately in the light of her decision.

Such a situation would raise questions not only of autonomy but of accountability, something stressed by several respondents.

I would advise her in these circumstances, and make sure she knew possible outcome if she still refused, and that I would not be held responsible.

If she still absolutely refused then this would be documented and full responsibility would be laid on her.

We ... would advise we cannot be responsible for the consequences. This can take a lot of time to get across to parents.

I would not insist, but I would make her and her husband aware of their account-ability for their decisions.

Whether a midwife can abjure responsibility completely in this situation is open to question. Some clearly found it hard to decide what a 'duty of care' might involve: one said while she would not insist, she 'would coerce with lots of persuasion if clear evidence of an at risk fetus.' The need for a woman to make an informed choice was pointed out by several: if the midwife considers the woman not to be informed, can this be used to override the woman's expressed wishes? One stated:

I would rarely insist, but very strongly recommend where there is evidence of fetal compromise (not just the risk of). If client was unable to make an informed choice, i.e. drink or drugged or insane then I might insist ... (duty of care to fetus).

One midwife who said she would not insist, added 'but the doctor may'. In such a case, who would put the monitoring straps on the woman? Clearly if the woman refuses outright, to attempt to use EFM could constitute an assault, and should be unthinkable. There were many who put very forcefully their view that to insist is not the right of the midwife.

I would never insist, that is not my right.

'Insist' is not a word in my vocabulary.

This is clearly a thorny issue. Many midwives appear to feel that they may somehow be deemed to be negligent if they do not carry out EFM in certain circumstances, particularly if unit protocols advocate its use. While good communication and explanation will reduce the likelihood of an antagonistic situation, conflict may still arise when views clash. A midwife's best recourse, having explained fully why she is advocating a particular procedure, but still meeting refusal, is to document this thoroughly, if possible with witnesses, and then carry out optimum care under those circumstances.

Invasive obstetric technology

Talk of interventions led onto a question about 'invasive obstetric technology', another phrase used by Beech (1984), who claimed that its proliferation is at its greatest in Britain, the clear implication being that the level is too high. The notion that such technology is either beneficial or necessary has been questioned (Flamm, 1990), particularly since the matter of control is seen by some to be handed to practitioners when such technology becomes commonplace (Mander, 1993).

Respondents were asked whether they felt the level of invasive obstetric technology to be too high, firstly in their own unit, and secondly in Britain as a whole. Almost a fifth (n=41) of the doctors agreed that the level is too high within their own unit. All but two of these came from units of more than 2,000 deliveries a year, and 21 of the 41 were from units of more than 3,500 deliveries a year. This corresponds closely to the responses given by midwives from different size units. However, with the exception of those practising obstetrics for less than three years, there was little difference in the responses when by analysed by length of experience.

Whereas almost a fifth had felt that the level of invasive obstetric technology is too high within their own units, almost a third felt this to be true of Britain as a whole (Fig. 6.8). The midwives' responses are also shown (Fig. 6.9); rather more midwives felt such technology to be at a too high level both generally and in Britain as a whole.

Figure 6.8   Doctors: do you agree that invasive obstetric technology is at a too high level a) in your own unit; b) in Britain as a whole?

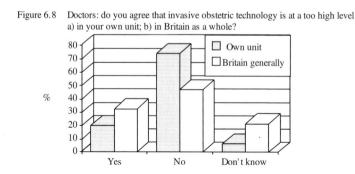

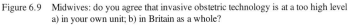

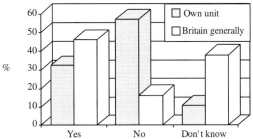

Figure 6.9   Midwives: do you agree that invasive obstetric technology is at a too high level
a) in your own unit; b) in Britain as a whole?

In relation to such technology within their own unit, there was a significant difference in midwives' responses according to their length of experience.

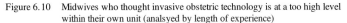

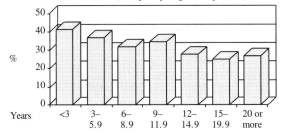

Figure 6.10   Midwives who thought invasive obstetric technology is at a too high level within their own unit (analsyed by length of experience)

It should be remembered that more of the junior midwives are employed within the larger units, which, as Fig. 6.11 shows, are more likely to have respondents argue that obstetric technology is too high. On the other hand this picture may reflect a trend among younger midwives which shows an increasing desire to emphasize the normality of midwifery and a corresponding distrust of technology.

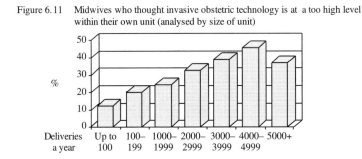

Figure 6.11   Midwives who thought invasive obstetric technology is at a too high level within their own unit (analysed by size of unit)

It is not surprising to find those midwives in the smaller units less likely to agree with this view, since the use of such technology there is comparatively low; nevertheless, a small number still thought the level to be too high. Within the larger units much more technology is used, although it is interesting to note that the midwives in the largest units were slightly less likely to agree than some colleagues in smaller units. Perhaps most notable is that at no stage do a majority of midwives appear to feel obstetric technology to be too high in their own unit.

For those who thought invasive technology to be too high, I asked for some examples.

Table 6.4:

Examples of invasive obstetric technology whose use is too high

Doctors	(n=)	%	Midwives	(n=)	%
CTG	35	17	Continuous CTG	287	16
Caesarean section	15	7	Induction of labour	187	10
Induction of labour	12	5.7	Caesarean sections	185	10
Ultrasound scans	3	1.4	Artificial rupture of membranes	139	8
Use of forceps	2	1	Fetal scalp electrodes	112	6
			Syntocinon	85	4.8
			Ultrasound scanning	82	4.6
			Fetal blood sampling	46	2.5
			Forceps	44	2.4
			Epidurals	32	1.8

Some of the procedures cited by midwives may not be considered to be invasive technology; some are invasive procedures, which some respondents obviously feel to be too prevalent. Again, many other examples were cited, including vaginal examinations, amniocentesis, chorion villus sampling, intrauterine pressure catheters, and episiotomy.

A common comment involved so-called 'social' inductions of labour, the notion being that labour is induced when a woman requests or demands it, regardless of the appropriateness of the procedure, or its likelihood of succeeding. Other comments were:

Augmentation taking place to suit daytime hours.

If you have a healthy infant in the end, invasive technology is never too high!

Obstetric input to normal pregnancy/delivery – intervention inevitable!!

Teaching hospitals have more invasive technology to help with teaching junior doctors.

Working in a 'high tech' unit means technology is used as first line management.

Some doctors added other comments to this question; they included the following by a GP, who claimed that he used no invasive obstetric technology.

None used – and no skills to use it either – could do with more expertise as a fall back for emergencies.

One SHO commented:

Overuse of CTGs in labour without proper training of midwives/doctors. Use of amniocentesis and AFP sampling in patients who, despite counselling, do not fully understand the implications of such tests.

Whether patients understand all of the procedures and tests which are offered during their pregnancy, and whether they can truly give informed consent, remains a moot point. The matter of staff training in CTG interpretation is discussed below.

Home birth vs hospital delivery

Another question in this section dealt with one of the thornier contemporary issues in maternity care – the question of place of delivery, specifically home versus hospital. This matter has not apparently had a great impact on litigation, but it is one area which focuses practitioners' minds with regard to matters such as choice, autonomy, and the normality of pregnancy and labour. These have already been discussed in this and the preceding chapter (cf. Thomson, 1991; Beazley, 1995; Jones and Smith, 1996). The House of Commons (1992) report on the Maternity Services noted the particular controversy surrounding this question: 'The issue of choice was most starkly highlighted by the debate over the place of birth' (*ibid.* para 74), and so it seemed an obvious area to tackle. Many clinicians consider home birth to be a high risk option, and therefore perhaps one area which may in time attract litigation.

Tew (1985) dismisses the assumption that hospital birth is safer because intervention is made easier, claiming that in fact perinatal mortality is higher in hospitals even allowing for their greater proportion of high risk pregnancies. While Campbell and MacFarlane (1986) criticize her statistical analysis, they do acknowledge that 'there is no evidence to support the claim ... that the safest policy is for all women to give birth in hospital'.

The question asked respondents whether they felt one place of delivery to be usually safer than the other. This was not in order to obtain absolute attitudes on which is the safer option, but to open the door to the question of safety, and to explore the concerns midwives and obstetricians have when calculating how best to accede to choice while providing what is thought to be good safe care. A supplementary question asked respondents to state the sort of dangers inherent in the option (hospital or home) they did not choose as being the safer. This question provoked a deluge of comments and anecdotes, particularly concerning the respective roles of Community midwives and GPs.

Perhaps unsurprisingly a large majority (91%) of the doctors answered that hospital birth is usually the safer; only seven respondents answered in favour of home birth (three of these were consultants, and two were GPs). Those hospital doctors who apparently favoured home births worked in all different sizes of unit. Reasons for advocating hospital birth were to do with a haemorrhaging mother and/or an asphyxiated baby. One consultant noted:

> The issue here is that the carnage of fetuses of home booked mothers becomes a hospital statistic when intrapartum transfer takes place.

One GP commented:

> Less willing to deliver moderate risk cases outwith consultant unit, i.e. I am asking my consultant colleagues to take cases that I might have delivered previously in the GP unit.

Those doctors who preferred home delivery mentioned the increased intervention likely to occur in hospitals, as well as lowered satisfaction rates for the families concerned. A much smaller proportion of the midwives agreed that hospital is usually the safer option: of the 1,740 who answered this question, 1,014 (58%) thought hospital to be usually safer, 500 (29%) thought not, and 226 (13%) weren't sure. There was little difference when answers were analysed by length of experience, but size of unit showed some discrepancy in those disagreeing that hospital birth is usually safer than home birth.

Figure 6.12   Hospital birth is not usually safer than home birth (midwives' answers analysed by size of unit)

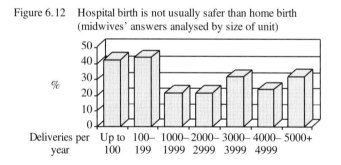

While the figure clearly shows a greater proportion in the smaller units thinking this way, over a quarter (27%) of all those in units with delivery rates of 3,000 or more also disagreed that hospital birth is not usually the safer. However the biggest variation was between those working in the Community, and an amalgamation of all those who gave their base as a consultant unit. Table 6.5 shows this.

Table 6.5:

Do you believe that hospital birth is usually safer than home birth?

	Yes	*No*	*Don't know*
Consultant unit midwives	795	287	169
	64%	*23%*	*14%*
Community midwives	125	135	35
	42%	*46%*	*12%*

This is a very marked difference of opinion,[1] which poses the question of how – especially in rural areas – pregnant women are to react to possibly conflicting advice. First consulting their local Community midwife to ask about home birth they may receive encouragement, but on attending a consultant unit are met with a much less enthusiastic response. Such differences of opinion may do little to increase respect in the overall service. The Scottish-English matched pairs analysis also produced a highly significant result: Yes answers were respectively 98 and 51. One midwife cited in the discussion on MRUs mentioned Scotland's 'medical establishment': it may well be that the particular influence of Scottish obstetricians in the development of maternity care in Scotland has had more of an effect on the attitudes of Scottish midwives than is the corresponding case with English obstetricians and English midwives.

The most commonly cited reasons for those who agreed that hospital birth is usually safer are shown in Table 6.6.

Table 6.6:

Midwives' most common reasons for believing hospital birth to be safer

Maternal/fetal emergency	623
Asphyxiated baby/Fetal distress	218
Ante-/intra-/post-partum haemorrhage	101
Distance from/delay getting to hospital	39

The largest single reason was a feeling that dealing with either a maternal or a fetal emergency would be more easily accomplished in hospital; others stated particular emergencies, as shown. Almost half of those who cited the distance between home and hospital were Community staff. This worry was evident from some of the comments, many of them from midwives based either in remote rural areas, or on an island.

Ambulance transport not always readily available.

Geographical situation especially in rural peninsulas; if emergency occurred greater delay in receiving emergency treatment.

---

1 It achieved a very high degree of significance: $p < .01^7$

Living on an island, important to access patient and if necessary transfer to mainland a.s.a.p.; time is important.

Distance from an obstetric unit if problems arise. Poor GP back up in some cases.

Home births are not encouraged in my community due to distance involved between client's home and main midwifery unit (over 100 miles), but a client wishing a home confinement would most certainly receive the very best possible attention.

The views of these Community midwives are very distinctive, and reflect situations and possible dangers not encountered by the majority of their colleagues in Britain. The disbanding of obstetric 'Flying Squads' in some areas, with obvious implications for rapid and experienced attention in an emergency, was mentioned by several.

A major concern was the screening of 'suitable' candidates for home delivery, and a perceived lack of experience among some Community staff; this was compounded by an apparent sense of alienation from hospital midwifery colleagues.

I suppose in many ways we had felt fairly safe in the Community, where we really only dealt with patients ante and post natally. With an impending home delivery of a patient with a very poor obstetric history it has really hit home hard. I requested to go into the hospital both to see a couple of deliveries and actually do one before the event. Because the hospital and community care are under different Trusts, authorisation had to be sought that the Community Trust would cover me for litigation while I was in the hospital. This is where the butterflies really started.

I do worry about litigation, and I feel in my area that Community Midwives are not kept up to date with clinical practice, procedures and policies ... we are never thought about like hospital midwives, we are forgotten. It should be compulsory that Community Midwives have an in-service update annually for one week; then I would feel more competent as a practitioner.

Many midwives I work with will be unhappy/refuse to provide services for home confinements as they are afraid of poor outcomes/litigation.

At the present time, I feel that the only occasion when I am concerned about litigation is with regards to home birth.

Community midwives are *not* allowed into Labour Ward at the maternity unit. Health Board policy is to discourage home deliveries due to 'geographical limitations'. When asked to help mothers who wish a home confinement, or those who consider Domino, my nurse manager informs me that I am a district nurse also and cannot give my maternity patients this commitment. Mothers have been visited in their home by the nurse manager and told that by wishing their Community Midwife in attendance they are in effect causing a district nurse to be away from her general patients.

The role of GPs and their relationship with Community midwives provided many comments. For some the relationship is a good one.

We relate effectively with GPs to a great extent and this allows us to practice true midwifery skills, with the comforting knowledge that GP back up is there if required.

The reality of living and working in a small community can be seen in a number of ways.

Working in an isolated GP unit we might be more vulnerable to litigation as we don't have medical and obstetric back up easily available, but in fact we get to know our families very well during the antenatal, intra and postnatal period, and therefore I believe women are less likely to sue if anything goes wrong.

I work in a GP unit in a small town. The midwives in the unit are well known which dispels a 'them and us' situation; this certainly helps when making difficult decisions, when an outcome is not going to be what you and the woman have anticipated (i.e. transfer to the consultant unit).

(I work) in a very remote small island community where everyone knows everyone else and relationships are generally very close and good.

I feel that being a midwife in a close-knit rural community that we are probably more afraid of the prospect of litigation because these patients are often close friends or neighbours, and we have to live with them as a community ... In the rural setting all too often the GP is the only emergency support available to the midwife, in the event of a problematic labour or pregnancy. 'Choices in Childbirth' are strictly limited in a rural community!

For many the midwife-GP relationship is a tense one:

A GP was ignorant of the fact that I as a professional midwife could take full responsibility for the antenatal care of my client, and send her into hospital without his consent.

It is the GPs who are negative about home confinements. GPs' writing is illegible, and is rarely signed: for obvious reasons.

The fear of litigation appears to be felt mostly among GPs, some of whom have little obstetric experience, but are unwilling to acknowledge midwives' responsibility and accountability and allow us to make decisions for which we have been trained.

The midwives in our team support women who wish home confinements, but the GPs actively discourage home confinements due to lack of their expertise and fear of litigation.

The apparent lack of obstetric experience among many GPs was a feature commonly noted.

Local GPs refer to consultants much more. Younger GPs not prepared to induce or augment labour because CTG not available.

Despite mums being deemed 'low risk' and booked for GP unit by the consultant, GPs will look for excuses to change bookings. Some examples are 'Thought to be a big baby', 'Thought to be a small baby' (despite scans estimating average weight);

rupturing membranes as soon as possible to see if they can find meconium; finding high blood pressures where there were none found by the midwife and none found on admission to the consultant unit. Granted, not all GPs are guilty of this. For those who are, the reason stated is that they are practising defensive medicine as they don't want to be sued!!

No women attached to my health practice are 'allowed' choice in home birth. There is no Domino facility or GP unit either – the health authority would like to give these choices, but our GPs are aggressively anti any choice ... As far as they are concerned, there is only one safe place – a consultant unit. All women wanting home birth have to find another GP. Not many take up this option. The local GP unit closed (a few years ago) because of GP opposition, not women's choice.

Fear of litigation has been frequently quoted by GPs in our area for limiting women's choices for care and place of confinement. Relationships between GP and midwife can be strained at times as midwife is seen to (be) 'encouraging' women to go against GP wishes or advice.

The fear of litigation, already mentioned by several, seems ever present for some.

It would appear that the second person at a home confinement should be a lawyer.

The fear of litigation I think will put midwives and GPs off the idea of safe delivery at home

However, as shown in Table 6.5, a significant proportion (particularly among community-based staff) stated they do not consider hospital birth to be usually safer than home birth. The most common reasons given are presented in Table 6.7.

Table 6.7:

Midwives' most common reasons for not believing hospital birth to be safer

Increased intervention	623
Increased infection	143
More maternal stress	130
Increased need for analgesia	51
Better continuity of care at home	40

The tendency in the hospital setting to apply protocols and to set time limits for labour was a frequent comment, usually leading to the most commonly cited reason, increased intervention. Again, many other comments were offered. The lack of a sense of control and privacy in the hospital setting was commonly noted, the woman being assumed to be subject to the following:

Domination of policies and procedures in hospital unit.

I simply cannot endorse hospital delivery as the 'safe option', where women are slotted into a routinised system with internecine communication problems and a hopelessly wide responsibility net. There is a spurious assumption of safety in routine which breeds an inability to cope should the woman not fit the mould.

Balancing the view (expressed above by a number of respondents) that hospital birth is safer due to the lack of recent intrapartum experience among community staff, several pointed out that a low level of experience in hospital midwives and doctors can cause just as many problems.

A few respondents pointed out that no one place of birth is safer *per se*; one detailed in part how the topic has become controversial, and how the situation could be approached:

> I feel home birth has been wrongly assumed by obstetricians to be less safe, because of their fear of the very rare 'catastrophes' which may occur. If a good obstetric flying squad was more available and midwives were all taught to site venflons, a lot of these perceived risks could be overcome.

There is no definitive answer to the question of hospital versus home, of course: each case must be considered individually. The range of views expressed does indicate a lively interest in this topic, however, with respondents divided on the merits and demerits of both home and hospital delivery.

Summary

- The question of a pregnant woman's autonomy remains divisive. Almost two-thirds of midwives, but less than half of the doctors, said they would insist on electronic fetal monitoring under certain circumstances, even when the woman had indicated she did not want this. A quarter of the midwives (and almost half of the doctors) said they would not insist. The concerns midwives have to ensure that the care they give cannot be regarded as negligent appears to influence their decisions significantly in this regard.

- Almost a third of midwives and almost a fifth of obstetricians felt the level of invasive obstetric technology to be too high within their own unit. This belief was much less prevalent among those midwives working in the smaller units; however more midwives in every size of unit except the very largest (over 5,000 deliveries a year) felt their unit to be better off in this regard than the situation in Britain as a whole.

- Consultant unit midwives and Community midwives differed significantly in their attitudes to home delivery, with hospital-based staff much more likely to conclude that hospital delivery is usually the safer option. Relationships between Community staff and their GP colleagues vary considerably: for many the home birth issue appears to be a focus for antagonism.

Part III
The Labour Period

CHAPTER SEVEN

Supervision and Control

Supervision

Inadequate supervision, both of patients and of junior staff, is a recurrent theme in investigations into poor clinical outcomes (UK Health Departments, 1996; Audit Commission, 1997; MCHRC, 1997) and has been cited as a feature of perinatal litigation (Doherty and James, 1994). The unpredictability of each day's workload in maternity care means that it can be difficult to guarantee that adequate staff are always available. Busier units with high stress levels may be more susceptible to high staff sickness rates, and so ensuring that sufficient staff are on duty can be problematic.

Respondents were asked about supervision of both patients and junior staff, and about the role of the consultant in the labour ward. First they were asked whether they felt supervision of patients within their unit to be inadequate. Options given were 'Frequently', 'Occasionally', 'Very rarely', and 'Never'.

Of the 1,664 midwives that answered this 205 (12%) opted for 'Frequently', 620 (37%) for 'Occasionally', 677 (41%) for 'Very rarely', and 161 (10%) for 'Never'. Analysis of those who answered 'Frequently' showed some interesting fluctuations – this option was chosen more by those who were less experienced.

Figure 7.1 Supervision of patients / clients is frequently inadequate (midwives' answers analysed by length of experience)

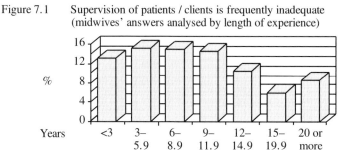

By size of unit there was an uneven positive association.

Figure 7.2 Supervision of patients / clients is frequently inadequate (midwives' answers analysed by size of unit)

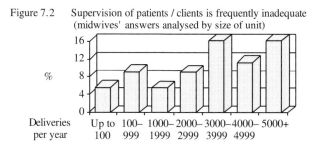

Most notable, however, was analysis by clinical grade: in this, the negative association between a higher grade and likelihood of answering 'Frequently' to this question is marked.

Figure 7.3   Supervision of patients / clients is frequently inadequate (midwives' answers analysed by grade)

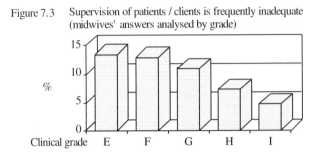

This indicates that the actual job done, rather than length of experience alone, may affect perceptions. In most units the bulk of direct patient care will be carried out by E and F grades (in Scotland at least), grades G and above having more of a supervisory role, perhaps being in charge of a ward or unit for that workshift. It might be thought that those in lower grades (E and F) may be more sensitive to patients' perceptions of supervision, since they are more often in direct contact with patients.

Those who answered 'Never' to this question were much more likely to be from the smaller units.

Figure 7.4   Supervision of patients / clients in our unit is never inadequate (midwives' answers analysed by size of unit)

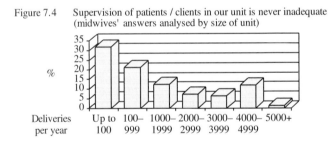

Very few of the doctors opted for Frequently or Never (11 and 15 respectively; none from England), with the vast majority choosing Occasionally (40%) and Very Rarely (47%). GPs were most likely to say Never, which perhaps reflects the nature of perinatal care in GP-run maternity units. Of the 11 doctors who claimed supervision is frequently inadequate, all were from Scottish units, and eight came from just three separate units. One of these three had an annual delivery rate of 3,500 and the others delivery rates of 5,000.

A much higher proportion of midwives (12% compared with five per cent in the obstetric survey) claimed that supervision of patients is frequently inadequate within their unit. As stated, these were more likely to be E and F grade midwives, qualified for less than 12 years, and working in larger units (3,000+ deliveries p.a.).

Respondents were then asked the same question with regard to supervision of junior staff within their own unit. Among midwives there appeared to be a sense that inadequate supervision was more of a problem for junior staff than for patients.

Figure 7.5   Supervision is inadequate: of patients and of junior staff (midwives' responses)

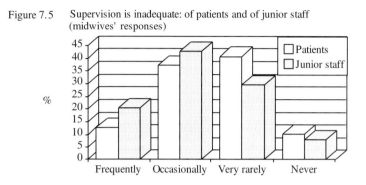

Once again the 'Frequently' option was more likely to be chosen by those on lower grades, and less likely to be chosen by those in smaller units. One respondent divided her answer to this question by distinguishing between junior medical and junior midwifery staff. Others commented on examples of inadequate supervision.

> Not enough extra staff to supervize. We had to deliver with Auxiliary helping. Very dangerous.

In the obstetricians' survey SHOs were far more likely than consultants (27% compared with five per cent) to say that such supervision is frequently inadequate.

Figure 7.6   Supervision of junior staff is frequently inadequate

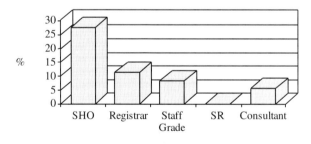

Calculation by Anova showed no difference in unit size between those who answered 'Frequently' and those who did not. More doctors as well as midwives cited 'Frequently' or 'Occasionally' for inadequate supervision of junior staff than for inadequate supervision of patients, but this was not statistically significant.

This led on to the claim made by Beech (1984) that women are often left completely alone for long periods during labour. One postnatal ward sister appeared to back up this claim, stating:

> Going by post natal debriefing, patients state they felt abandoned.

Reactions to this claim were heavily weighted towards disagreement, although six of the doctors (3%) and 75 (4.5%) of the midwives answered 'Frequently', and 13% and 19% respectively answered 'Occasionally'. Those who answered 'Frequently' came from units of varying sizes, although the numbers are comparatively small.

The Confidential Enquiry into Maternal Deaths (UK Health Departments, 1996) found that in 13 cases the failure to inform a consultant was a contributing factor. While this may represent an extreme situation, it may also be seen as the tip of the iceberg, for if junior staff feel somehow unable to contact a consultant in a dire emergency, will they do so in less critical (but still potentially serious) instances?

Consultant grade staff were asked whether they felt that in general they could rely on their junior colleagues to deal with potential or actual problems in the labour ward, and grades below consultant were asked whether they felt that in general they could rely on their consultant to provide adequate support in order to deal with such circumstances. Responses are shown in Figure 7.7.

Figure 7.7   Consultants: Can you rely on your junior staff to deal with actual
or potential problems in the labour ward?
Junior grades: Can you rely on your consultant to provide adequate support
in order to deal with potential or actual problems in the labour ward?

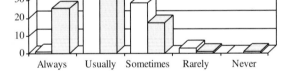

While most practitioners opted for the Usually/Sometimes answers, there was a striking difference in the numbers answering Always: only one consultant out of 91, compared with 27 junior grades out of 107.[1] Why the consultants should apparently be much less disposed to trust their junior colleagues in this situation than vice versa is not clear; it does beg the question about having a consultant presence on the labour ward at all times in order to deal with problems.

The Confidential Enquiry into Maternal Deaths (UK Health Departments, 1996) commented that 'it is evident that the establishment of consultant sessions for delivery unit supervision still falls far short of needs.' However in this survey only half the consultants felt that a permanent consultant presence on the labour ward (one of the specific recommendations of the Confidential Enquiry) was a good idea, and an even greater proportion of the junior grades were even less keen. Perhaps surprisingly 73%

---

1 This difference was highly significant: p<.00001

of the SHOs said they did not think this a good idea, placing the claims by Ennis (1991) concerning supervision in some context.

Many units appear now to be developing policies and protocols in order to standardize care and help prevent clinical errors. The possibility that such policies can help to minimize the risk of mistakes or actual negligence was put to the doctors. A large majority (86%) agreed that they could, with the consultants slightly more likely to agree than their junior colleagues. At one time it might have been thought that such protocols and policies would be resisted because they disallowed individual autonomous practice; the reality now appears to be that they are felt to be a major safeguard against allegations of substandard care or negligence.

Episiotomy

Midwives were also asked about episiotomies, the question being posed in a similar fashion to the one discussed in Chapter 6 concerning whether a practitioner could insist on performing electronic fetal monitoring. This question does not relate to doctors, since they are only likely to perform an episiotomy when conducting a forceps, ventouse or breech delivery, for which episiotomies are considered by many to be more or less mandatory. Midwives were asked whether there were any circumstances in which they would perform an episiotomy if a labouring woman had indicated that she did not want one. Unlike the previous question, the word 'insist' was not used here, although the distinction may be marginal.

This issue again poses questions concerning autonomy, the disregarding of which may predispose a patient to bring a complaint. Perineal trauma has been identified as a significant factor in perinatal litigation, and so this seemed a pertinent area to tackle.

Overall the proportions answering 'Yes' and 'No' to this question were very similar to those concerning the previous question. Of 1,714, 1,112 (65%) said they would perform an episiotomy under certain circumstances, 425 (25%) said they wouldn't, and 177 (10%) were unsure.

Figure 7.8   If a woman indicated that she did not want an episiotomy, are there any circumstances in which you would perform one?

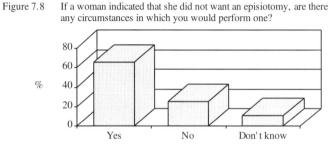

As with the previous question, concern may be raised about the discrepancy in opinions, and the implications this has for the idea of equal standards of care. If attitudes and standards vary (as they appear to from these answers) how is a pregnant woman to know where the midwife who is to deliver her stands? The development of team midwifery, with the theory of a pregnant woman meeting a small group of midwives, one of whom will deliver her, appears to offer the best option for the majority of women.

As Table 7.1 shows, there is not an exact correlation between those insisting on EFM and those who would perform an episiotomy when the woman had indicated she didn't want one.

Table 7.1:

If a woman indicated that she did not want an episiotomy,
are there any circumstances in which you would perform one?

	Yes	*No*	*Don't know*
Would insist on EFM under certain circumstances	76%	17%	7%
Would not insist on EFM	40%	48%	12%
Unsure	49%	25%	30%

As can be seen, a sixth (17%) of those who said they would insist on EFM would not perform an episiotomy if the woman refused it, and two-fifths of those who would not insist on EFM would perform an episiotomy under certain circumstances even if the woman had indicated she did not want one; so although Figures 6.4 and 7.8 look very similar, it is not the same midwives who comprise each of the groups answering Yes, No or Don't Know.

Table 7.2:

Most commonly cited reasons by midwives for performing an episiotomy
even when the woman has indicated she does not want one

Fetal distress	982
Rigid perineum/risk of third degree tear	222
Shoulder dystocia	111
Preterm labour	79
Previous third degree tear	52
Prolonged second stage	51

Fetal distress was by far the most commonly cited reason, and there was a slightly greater tendency to cite this amongst those midwives qualified less than nine years than those above.

Figure 7.9 Proportion of midwives who cited fetal distress as a reason for performing an episiotomy (analysed by length of experience)

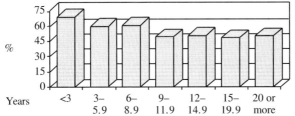

The association between length of experience of those who gave their place of work as the labour ward and citing fetal distress is shown in Figure 7.10. There is no consistent correlation, with, interestingly, the most senior midwives more likely to cite fetal distress than some of their junior colleagues.

Figure 7.10 Proportion of labour ward staff who cited fetal distress (analysed by length of experience)

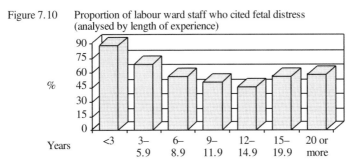

Other reasons for performing an episiotomy included 'To prevent a forceps delivery', 'breech', 'big baby', 'cord prolapse', 'maternal distress', and 'haemorrhage'. Once again, many other comments were added.

Cannot force a woman to have any procedure unless you want to be sued for battery and assault.

Fetal distress is the only research based reason for performing episiotomy.

I had one client recently who refused steadfastly, but as there was fetal distress I finally persuaded her to agree after a length of time.

This is difficult as the responsibility is for both mother and baby, and where fetal hypoxia is imminent. You could legally be in trouble either way.

Would discuss need – document in case notes and request second person in room to witness refusal.

The need for the woman's autonomy to be considered, and the need to give adequate information so that she can make an informed choice, was mentioned several times. The dilemma felt by many midwives in a situation where severe fetal distress occurs came through strongly in their comments. One midwife who said she would carry out an episiotomy added:

> If I was so concerned about the fetus and I thought it was worth being taken to court over!!

Another explained how she would deal with such a situation.

> Most women are 'reasonable' when full discussion is undertaken … If, after discussion, a woman categorically refused episiotomy under any circumstances, then I would inform the senior midwife and would expect the woman to sign her name to her wishes and perhaps ask her husband to countersign.

The question of who may accept the responsibility for countermanding a woman's expressed wish was discussed by a third:

> I would discuss the reasons for performing an episiotomy beforehand to ensure she had not been misinformed. If she was well informed and still refused I would seek medical advice and only perform one under superior instruction.

The next question dealt with the respondent's personal episiotomy rate. Concern has been expressed by consumer groups about the rate of episiotomy, and so it seemed appropriate to ask what the respondent believed her own rate to be, and secondly to ask about the rate within her unit. The range of answers was great: personal episiotomy rates varied from 0% to 90%, as did perceived unit rates. Overwhelmingly respondents felt their own rate to be below the average for their unit. Figure 7.11 shows the respective rates for those who gave a rate for both themselves and their unit. The first column shows the respondent's own rate, while the second shows the average unit rate for those who claimed that particular personal rate.

Figure 7.11   Own episiotomy rate compared with perceived unit rate

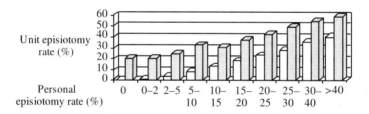

Of the 965 who gave a figure for both themselves and their unit, only 16 (1.6%) gave their own rate as higher than average; a further 61 (6.3%) said their rate and the unit rate were the same. The remaining 888 (92%) said their own rate was below the average for their unit, and, as can be seen from Figure 7.11, as a respondent's perceived personal rate increased, so, correspondingly, did the perceived unit rate. The ratio ranged from a marginal difference to several times the difference, the bulk being up to five times.

The huge variation in estimates indicated that some respondents do not appear to have very accurate figures to hand. While it is entirely feasible for the ratio of personal rate to unit rate to be above 20 in some instances, for such a large majority to feel that their own rate was below the average (usually several factors below) seems a little immodest,

Figure 7.12   Ratio (own episiotomy rate to unit rate) for those whose own
rate is below unit average

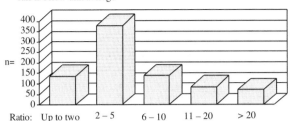

even allowing for the fact that forceps deliveries will increase the unit rate by a certain amount – unless the bulk of episiotomies are attributed to non-responders to this questionnaire, or to students (whom I did not survey). Wilkerson (1984) and Begley (1986) do show that individual rates vary enormously, and without specifying other variables (such as parity) comparisons between individuals can be misleading.

In some cases the estimates of unit rate appeared to be rather wild: it is certainly to be hoped that no unit now has an episiotomy rate above 50%, although this claim was made by several. A study by Garcia et al (1985) found hugely differing rates between different consultant units (from less than 20% to 79%). Macfarlane and Mugford (1984) found a steady increase in the rate from 25% in 1967 to 53% in 1978, but this is a little out of date now. Few figures are available, and most of those that are relate to the late 1970s or early-mid 1980s (Kitzinger and Walters, 1981; Sleep, 1984; Begley, 1986), since when it is claimed that episiotomy is a far less common procedure. A more recent study (Logue, 1991) describes how strategies to reduce episiotomy rates have been effective in one north London hospital (39% in 1981 to 12% in 1987). Although no comprehensive data are now published, a telephone poll of ten units within Scotland revealed a range of rates from 11% to 28% for normal deliveries, with an average of 18.4%. Without more information such statistics could be misleading, although it is unlikely that the demographic makeup of pregnant women in each area would influence the rate significantly.

This would certainly indicate that the overall rate is now far lower than it once was, although – many would claim – still not low enough. The variation in rate is hard to explain without more information; certainly there would appear to be considerable room for rate reduction programmes, along the lines described by Logue, in some units.

While perineal trauma does appear to be a significant factor in complaints and subsequent litigation, in fact the substance of such claims generally refers to the repair of the perineum. James (1991) notes that settling such claims can be extremely expensive. One midwife commented:

> Resuturing of episiotomy/tear – something I do fairly often. The fear of litigation makes me nervous and stressed, maybe with time and experience though my confidence in this area will increase.

It would certainly be enlightening to discover what the level of training concerning perineal repair is throughout the country. Such research could assist in determining a 'gold standard' towards which units could aspire. The beneficial effects in terms of improved care and outcome, and the subsequent reduction in health service costs (in terms of further hospitalisations and litigation) could be significant.

Summary

- Few obstetricians felt supervision of patients to be frequently inadequate within their unit; more thought supervision of junior staff to be frequently inadequate – a considerable divergence of opinion between consultants and SHOs was noted in these replies.

- 12% of midwives claimed supervision of patients is frequently inadequate within their unit, and another 37% claimed this is occasionally true; midwives who are grades E and F were much more likely to cite 'frequently' than their more senior colleagues. The possible implications, in terms of substandard care and poor outcome, may have serious legal as well as personal consequences.

- 65% of the midwives said they would, under certain circumstances, perform an episiotomy even if the labouring woman had said she did not want one. Perceived personal episiotomy rates were far lower than the perceived unit rate (mostly by a factor of between two and five).

- Consultants were much less likely to say they could always rely on their junior colleagues to deal with labour ward problems than junior staff were to say they could always rely on their consultants to provide adequate support in such circumstances. The prospect of a permanent consultant presence on the labour ward was, however, much less favoured by SHOs and registrars.

CHAPTER EIGHT

Fetal Monitoring

Monitoring of fetal wellbeing in labour

This aspect of perinatal care is of critical medico-legal importance, and has been debated at great length. There is a large literature on the subjects of CTG monitoring – also known as Electronic Fetal Monitoring (EFM) – and fetal blood sampling (FBS), particularly the former. Its place in current practice has been debated, from the point of view of poor outcomes (MCHRC, 1997) as well as legal implications (Capstick and Edwards, 1990). An escalating caesarean section rate has been claimed by some to be due in part to an increase in CTG use (Francome, 1986); levels of ability to interpret results are said to fluctuate (Ennis and Vincent, 1990; Dover and Gauge, 1995); and outcome measures appear to fail to make the case for routine monitoring, even in high risk patients (Haverkamp et al, 1976; Luthy et al, 1987), or with regard to the incidence of cerebral palsy (Grant et al, 1989). More recently others have called for mandatory use of continuous EFM in the presence of certain factors (Gaffney et al, 1994).

Practitioners themselves are divided over the desirability of using CTG machines in labour, and there have been calls from some user groups to minimize the role of such technology with its consequent likelihood of increasing intervention.

It was asked whether respondents felt CTG monitoring to be overused, underused, or about right within their unit. Thirty-seven per cent of the doctors and 42% of the midwives felt it to be overused, with just 4% and 1% respectively claiming it is underused. Middle grade staff (senior registrars, registrars and staff grades) were most likely to say that it is overused.

Figure 8.1   What do you feel about CTG monitoring in your unit?

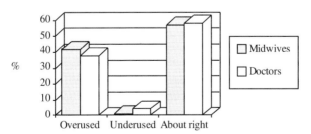

As with the midwifery questionnaire, a larger proportion of the Scottish doctors claimed that CTG is overused (40% compared with 29% of the English doctors). The Scottish-English midwifery matched pairs trial again showed some difference, with 81 in Scotland and 47 in England replying that CTG monitoring is overused in their unit.[1]

---

1 Again, this was highly significant: p. < .0001

Without knowing how prevalent the rates are in different units in Scotland and England such answers are of course particularly subjective: it may be that CTG use is far more common or routine in Scotland.

There have been suggestions that CTG monitoring without fetal blood sampling (FBS) is worthless, because the heart rate is only one indicator of fetal wellbeing/distress, and in any situation where distress is suspected, a blood sample may help either to confirm or refute that diagnosis (van den Berg et al, 1987). This is not a universal view, however; it can be pointed out that the sample comes from what may be a bruised part of the scalp, and so may not be representative; neither can it conclude that distress/acidosis will not occur soon after the sample is taken. This procedure is less common than CTG monitoring – indeed many smaller units do not carry it out at all.

Respondents were asked about FBS within their unit. Very few of the doctors (8%) thought it overused, but a third thought it underused. This compared with 15% and 13% respectively among midwives, although interesting to note was a much higher rate of answering 'Overused' in the Scottish sub-sample (25 compared with 8). At first glance this reflects the response to the previous question, but with FBS comparatively rare compared to CTG use, this difference is harder to explain.

With moves now to obtaining cord blood samples for routine blood gas analysis after delivery in an attempt to provide retrospective evidence of fetal wellbeing, it may be that the desire to carry out FBS will be lessened. There will still be the need to carry out this procedure in certain cases, and courts may still look to the timing and the results of such tests in determining questions of causation (for instance in cases where brain damage in an infant has occurred).

Respondents were asked whether in general it is desirable for a woman to be continuously monitored in labour. While MacDonald et al (1985) point out that there is no consensus of opinion about this when the baby is deemed to be at risk, Murphy et al (1990) note that continuous CTG use has somehow become integral to obstetric practice. In broad terms the argument lies between the desire to have a constant indicator of fetal wellbeing, and a desire to allow mobility and so encourage the normal process of labour. The question was deliberately phrased in such a broad way to allow for comments to be made, and several were.

Few respondents agreed that it is desirable to have continuous monitoring: 16% of the doctors compared with 79% saying it is not desirable (4% answered 'Don't Know'). There was little difference between the grades, except that all the GPs said it is not desirable. Even fewer of the midwives (5%) favoured continuous monitoring.

Many comments were added to this question.

Table 8.1:
Most common comments by midwives about CTG use

Used more than necessary	106
Only needed if high risk	75
Intermittent is enough	31
Overuse de-skills	26
Causes intervention	25
Restricts mobility	23

There were many more comments, most of which were unclassifiable in this way. Some were obviously in favour of CTGs, or at least found them very useful.

All patients should be monitored in late first stage and second stage.

Some clients feel safer being continually (*sic*) monitored.

Sometimes it is easier to attach a monitor to a woman rather than stay with her.

The woman may wish monitoring if she was looked after this way previously.

Yes (to continuous monitoring) – only from a purely selfish viewpoint, i.e. convenience!

Others were of a different opinion.

CTG – overused; good midwifery practice – underused.

Has not been shown to reduce perinatal mortality rate; it should not be used unless facilities for fetal blood sampling are also available.

Machines often inaccurate.

Midwives often use CTG and forget about their own midwifery skills.

Some worried about CTG use making them defensive or over-cautious.

Always the worry of litigation. Mothers reassured by hearing FH.

CTGs left to run 'just in case'.

I feel it is tempting if the woman has to be left for a long time – continuous monitoring is used to keep the midwife happy.

The insistence of use by unit protocol or common practice was a fairly common theme.

Birth plans are issued and the client wishes to mobilize, but superior in charge insists on monitoring!

I don't always perform continuous CTGs. If I'm in the midwife led part of the labour ward I can do my own thing. If I'm looking after 'non midwife-led' women, I feel pressurized by the sisters on labour ward to perform continuous monitoring.

I believe hospital staff midwives monitor continually to appease individual consultants' concern, not necessarily because it is indicated maternally, particularly the just qualified staff.

Habit! We do admission CTGs, give analgesia – before you know, you can't take it off.

Interpretation of traces was also a common theme.

Midwives who tend to electronically monitor labour have difficulty reading the trace anyway.

Show me the substantial evidence for CTG interpretation or two 'experts' who interpret the same recordings in the same way.

CTGs rarely seem accurate – in conjunction with blood gases and other factors one may better assess the information. Reading a CTG on its own is not very useful.

We are still learning about CTGs. Doctors like them, midwives worry about taking them off once they are on, women don't seem to have strong feelings for or against – some find it comforting and not too inconvenient.

One midwife summed up a dilemma posed by CTGs.

Since the introduction of electronic fetal monitoring the involvement of medical staff in normal labours must have increased by 500% due to the midwife being obliged to report any 'deviations'. The withdrawal of monitors would leave the midwives open to the claim of negligence if the outcome was adverse.

Comments by doctors added included the following from a GP.

Not desirable to have a woman continuously monitored in labour. But greater swift access to expertise in an emergency would be a Godsend; also training (organized and funded) to maintain and enhance the basic level of skills we do have.

One SHO claimed that:

CTG is reassuring when satisfactory, and provides hard evidence of fetal condition during labour. It may be important to fall back on should a litigation case arise.

A Consultant countered this view.

No: There is too much monitoring in labour for no proven benefit. It causes a great deal of patient and professional anxiety, largely driven by fear of litigation.

Another SHO highlighted the tension between wanting to allow a normal labour, and also wanting 'hard copy' of the fetal condition in case something unexpectedly goes wrong.

Depends on view of mother and circumstances of labour. In a normally progressing labour with no epidural or other adverse circumstances, continuous monitoring is not necessary. However, the risk of an unrecognized intrapartum event may arise and there is then no objective evidence with which to discuss the case.

This SHO hints that there are occasions ('epidural or other adverse circumstances') when CTG monitoring should always be used, and this situation has been discussed with reference to whether staff can insist on such procedures.

Safety of EFM

Concern has been expressed that using EFM does not contribute to an improved neurological outcome for the infant (Shy et al, 1990), and this study has been interpreted as indicating that EFM may in fact predispose infants to cerebral palsy (Beech, 1992), although no hard evidence for this is apparent. The next question asked whether it was felt that EFM is completely safe (i.e. has no adverse sequelae). Given the prevalence of this procedure it was interesting to note that a majority of doctors answered 'No'.

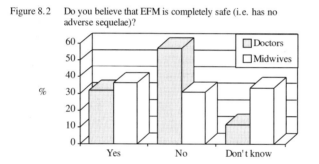

Figure 8.2   Do you believe that EFM is completely safe (i.e. has no adverse sequelae)?

Among doctors there was no consistent association between grade or length of experience and answering this question, but there was some difference between different grades of midwife; however, given the much smaller numbers of the higher grades this should be interpreted with caution.

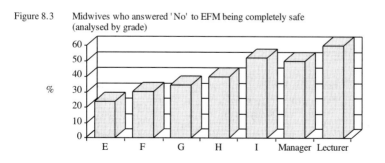

Figure 8.3   Midwives who answered 'No' to EFM being completely safe (analysed by grade)

Given the prevalence of CTG monitoring – and it would appear from some of the comments that its use is regarded as mandatory in some units – it is disturbing to find that a significant proportion of practitioners seem unconvinced about its safety. For only 32% of doctors and 36% of midwives to be able to answer that they consider it completely safe raises questions about the practitioner's role as the patient's advocate. Unfortunately the survey did not probe respondents' views as to why they believed EFM not to be completely safe; this could form the basis of further research.

Interpretation of CTGs

Ranjan (1993) points out that a number of legal cases have hinged on the time delay between recognizing distress and acting upon it. While the ability to recognize distress is an obvious prerequisite to taking action, Vincent et al (1991) claim that, 'It is clear that some junior doctors and midwives cannot recognize abnormal CTG traces.' Certainly some legal cases have claimed that CTG abnormalities have been ignored or not noticed (Ennis and Vincent, 1990). Ennis (1991) further points out that in a survey of 26 obstetric SHOs, by the end of their six-month post half had received no formal training in CTG interpretation.

Interpretation of CTGs has been shown to vary not only between individual practitioners (Scottish Office, 1994), but also when the same practitioner examines the same trace twice (Nielsen et al, 1987). Doherty and James' dictum that 'CTG traces are only as valuable as those who interpret them' (1994) appears both curt and accurate. In the light of these findings it seemed pertinent to ask how confident respondents were in their ability to assess fetal distress in an intrapartum CTG. Although 'fetal distress' as a term is now being superseded in an attempt to be more accurate (practitioners are now encouraged to talk of fetal acidosis – as measured by scalp pH – or describe a particular fetal heart rate abnormality), it is still widely used and its broad meaning commonly understood.

A range of possible rates (of probability of being able to assess intrapartum fetal distress accurately) was given, from 50% to 100% in 5% intervals. A few respondents (nine doctors and seven midwives) ticked the 50% box, adding 'Less than' above it. The full range of answers was used, and it was interesting to note that, overall, the confidence of midwives appeared higher than that of the doctors (Fig. 8.4).

Confidence in the ability to interpret traces appears high among midwives, with over half the sample apparently able to assess fetal distress at least 75% of the time. Interesting to note was the fact that while 9.7% of those who gave their work place as the labour ward claimed either 95 or 100%, more likely to claim this were those in the antenatal/postnatal/clinics area (11.5%) and those in team or rotation schemes (11.8%).

It should be borne in mind that an abnormal fetal heart rate tracing does not necessarily indicate distress (as measured either by FBS or the baby's condition upon immediate

Figure 8.4   How would you rate the probability that you could accurately assess fetal distress in an intrapartum CTG?

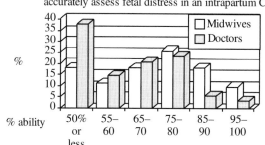

delivery), although in practice the connection seems to be assumed. One doctor commented that:

> Over diagnosis of 'distress' is a large problem.

From the midwife's point of view there came this comment.

> It can be very frustrating for midwives to inform doctors of a suspected abnormality, to have it ignored before client, and to have to repeatedly call the doctor back. It is also difficult for midwives to overrule, disagree with a doctor's decision unless they are prepared to take it higher, e. g. consultant level.

Ennis and Vincent (1990) note that in some of the legal cases which they analysed, midwives had correctly noted a fetal heart rate abnormality, but this was ignored by the doctor. Reflecting the concerns raised by Vincent et al (1991) above, moves towards improving practitioners' understanding of CTG traces have been introduced in many areas. Doctors were asked whether they felt there was sufficient training, first of all of junior obstetricians, and then of midwifery staff, in this matter.

Regarding junior obstetric staff, overall answers were fairly evenly split, although there was a large difference between grades in those answering that training is insufficient.

Figure 8.5   Training of junior obstetric staff in CTG interpretation is insufficient

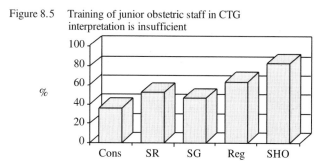

The different proportions of Consultants and SHOs answering respectively 'Sufficient' and 'Insufficient' was highly significant[2]. Clearly there is a gap in perception in this

---

2 $p < .01$ (analysis by Chi-square)

matter, and until steps are taken to improve the confidence of junior staff, there is always the danger that errors in interpretation will occur with perhaps devastating consequences in terms of outcome, and possible legal repercussions.

A higher proportion of obstetricians (65%) felt training of midwives to be insufficient (only 20% said it was sufficient), and this belief was echoed in the midwifery questionnaire. Midwives were asked what level of training in CTG interpretation they had had since qualifying. These were 'open answer' questions, and produced a lower response rate than might have been gained from offering a series of options. In all, 1,181 provided answers; the 'While training' section answers were almost all along the lines of 'From qualified staff' and 'In college', but the 'Since qualifying' section produced a wider range of answers. The most common are shown in Table 8.2.

Table 8.2:
Midwives' most commonly cited levels of training in
CTG interpretation since qualifying

In service: with or without lectures	327
At least one study day	263
Minimal	226
None	212
Self taught	179
From colleagues	147
Regular updates	135

Some respondents gave more than one answer, and many other comments were offered. A feeling of inadequacy regarding this aspect of care was obvious from certain comments.

> Attended one day course 8 years ago.

> None – have asked for more.

> Not enough.

> Yearly session. Discussion of case studies.

> On the hoof!

> Basic.

It is impossible to know exactly what level of training in-service education offers, as this is likely to vary between different units. Perhaps more worrying is that of those working in the labour ward, only 14% said they had regular updates, less than a quarter (24%) had been on a study day, 8% said their level of training had been minimal, and 5% said they had had none at all. This must be a matter for concern, for it is the midwife who will usually first pick up on possible problems, the SHO being the usual first line of reference when requesting medical advice. If a large proportion of both these groups feel that their training has been inadequate (the confidence of many midwives notwithstanding), the impression of a disaster waiting to happen is easily conjured.

The Apgar score

Courts have looked at the subject of asphyxia when dealing with cases involving a handicapped child. The next two questions looked at Apgar scoring (Apgar, 1953), for more than 40 years the method whereby the condition of the newborn baby has been assessed (this being with regard to the five criteria of heart rate, colour, reflex response, muscle tone, and respiratory effort). At first glance a fairly objective test, it has been seen in practice to cause considerable disagreement, and its predictive value for severe handicap shown to lack sensitivity (Nelson and Ellenberg, 1981; Levene et al, 1986; Ruth and Raivio, 1988). Marlow (1992) in fact questions whether we still need the Apgar score.

Blair (1993) notes 'the difficulty of reaching a clinically operational definition of birth asphyxia', but despite this the procedure is still almost universal, and courts may consider the Apgar scores when assessing whether a newborn baby has been asphyxiated (and if so, to what degree). It seemed pertinent then to ask whether it is seen as an objective test after all.

It was asked whether midwives are consistent when using the Apgar score (again, this does not relate directly to obstetricians). 1,013 out of 1,755 (58%) thought so, with 484 (28%) disagreeing, and 256 (15%) unsure. Grade appeared to matter little in this respect, and nor did length of experience. However there was some difference noted when answers were analysed by size of unit, with those in the largest units (more than 5,000 deliveries a year) less likely to agree.

The next question asked whether midwives score the same as paediatricians. Far fewer agreed with this: 26%, while 49% disagreed, and 25% were unsure. Quite why there should be such a discrepancy between what midwives and what paediatricians are perceived to give as a score is unclear, although a few comments were made.

No two people score the same.

Paediatricians are often not present to give the one-minute Apgar score, and yet if called for an emergency they sometimes fill in a one-minute score!

Depends on the paed.'s experience – junior = lower Apgar scores.

The last quoted midwife indicates that junior paediatricians are believed to give lower scores than their more experienced colleagues. For such a supposedly objective scoring system to be apparently so subjective may cause concern. It would appear that continuing education is required in order to iron out any differences caused by a lack of understanding of the nature of the test. Anecdotally, it appears that some one-minute scores are low because the practitioner scores the baby just seconds after the delivery rather than waiting for one minute of age.

Summary

- 37% of doctors and 42% of midwives felt CTG monitoring is overused within their unit; belief in overuse was much more common among the Scottish respondents from both clinical groups. 82% of the SHOs felt that training in CTG interpretation for junior staff was insufficient, and 59% of the consultants felt that such training for midwives was also insufficient.

- It was worrying to find that only a minority of both midwives and obstetricians believed EFM to be completely safe. If practitioners are acting as the 'patient's advocate', are they honestly giving her their opinion about electronic monitoring? Given its widespread use, this area needs to be addressed.

- Midwives' perceived ability to assess fetal distress in an intrapartum CTG, despite many based in the labour ward saying they had received little or no training, was considerably higher than that of the doctors. This generally high degree of confidence notwithstanding, levels of training in this art vary considerably, and for many labour ward-based midwives such training appears to be either inadequate or non-existent. Given the importance of CTG traces in perinatal legal matters, this is an issue which needs to be addressed. Formal mandatory CTG workshops and assessment of individual skills would seem to be the minimum steps hospitals must take.

- There was considerable disagreement about the Apgar score. In theory this is an objective test, but in practice there would appear to be considerable room for differences of opinion. This may cause medico-legal problems, since the Apgar score may be looked to in legal cases to determine whether there was an appropriate response by staff to a situation where asphyxia may have been present.

Part IV
Communication, Complaints and Counselling

CHAPTER NINE

Communication and Rapport

Communication and rapport between practitioners and patients is essential for good care (UK Health Departments, 1996), particularly when a situation falls short of its ideal. Doherty and James (1994) note that 'many claims arise from failures of communication or resentment ... failure to treat patients with courtesy and respect may fuel resentment', while in their study Dingwall and Fenn (1991) maintain that when claims were received, some staff 'seem to have been concerned to do the minimum necessary to respond to the grievance'. Because of evidence of poor communication in cases which result in litigation, Vincent et al (1994b) claim that 'training in communication skills ... is urgently needed.'

It is clear that such improvements have been a target of many providers of maternity services, although it may be argued that the focus has been on organizational rather than interpersonal communication. Examples are user-held records, 'pregnancy clubs' to replace traditional parentcraft sessions, tours for toddlers, and a barrage of leaflets about the services and choices available to local women and their families (DoH, 1993b).

Respondents were asked how they would rate communication and rapport in their unit first of all generally, and secondly when something has gone wrong.

Table 9.1:

Doctors: How would you rate communication and rapport between patient and practitioner in your unit?

	Very good	Good	Fair	Poor	Terrible
generally	46	143	21	0	0
	22%	68%	10%	0%	0%
when something has gone wrong	33	133	37	6	0
	16%	64%	18%	3%	0%

Table 9.2:

Midwives: How would you rate communication and rapport between patient and practitioner in your unit

	Very good	Good	Fair	Poor	Terrible
generally	551	1024	164	7	1
	31%	*58%*	*9%*	*0.4%*	*0.06%*
when something has gone wrong	327	869	438	83	9
	19%	*50%*	*25%*	*5%*	*0.5%*

There is a slight 'downward' shift in relationships with patients when things go wrong; midwives tended to be more pessimistic in such circumstances. However it is precisely when things go wrong that communication and rapport need to be sound and reliable. This, it is claimed, may lessen the incidence of litigation (Dingwall, 1991). At the very least it should serve as part of good care; the setting up of Birth Afterthoughts (Charles and Curtis, 1994; Smith and Mitchell, 1996) has been one practical example of this.

Little variation was noted when analysing the first part by size of unit or length of experience. Things change slightly when something has gone wrong, with clinical grades E, F, G and H a little less likely to characterize communication as 'Good' or 'Very good' than I grades or Managers; however numbers in these last two groups are small, and statistical tests unreliable. Nevertheless it is apparent that there is a downward shift in perceptions when things are not going well, and it is worrying that one in 20 respondents thought communication and rapport to be either 'Poor' or 'Terrible' in such a situation. A number of legal cases refer to situations where the tragedy of a poor outcome has been compounded by a perceived failure on the part of practitioners to counsel patients and explain events (Vincent et al, 1994a; Symon, 1997e).

There were some differences between the responses of the Scottish and English matched pairs, with the English more likely to characterize relationships generally as 'Very Good', and as 'Good/Very Good' when something has gone wrong. Many respondents felt this to be an important area, as the attached comments showed.

I believe poor communication to be a main factor in the rise in litigation. Parents may often just want the truth, what really happened.

Communication is of the utmost importance in our profession. This in general is poor ... In my experience most people's anger in the case of negligence is that they cannot get straight answers from the people involved, and indeed often cannot get to speak to them; this in turn makes them feel that there is some sort of 'cover up'.

It seems to me that parents sue a) in an effort to get more information about what happened to them if staff do not honestly answer their questions, or b) if they have a child who is going to need constant care for many years ... I think that people generally accept that we are all human beings and that we do make mistakes, sometimes with disastrous consequences. It amazes me that more people don't sue but are able to accept explanations and apologies which are honestly and sincerely given. I suspect that more women will begin suing in relation to post traumatic stress disorder in the next few years.

Although the ideal would be clear lines of communication, in practice there may be obstacles to this.

In my experience 'breakdowns in communication' have occurred when the husband or partner has become exhausted. Nerves are frayed and they are often less well informed about Labour Room procedures than the women. This is when the midwife is likely to be obstructed from performing her normal duties ... it can alter the outcome of a perfectly normal labour.

I find it very difficult to estimate how much patients understand what you are telling them, even if you ask them directly if they understand. Often days or even weeks later if you meet them they begin asking questions which you know you have already explained. I know that pregnancy and delivery and the post natal period are a very emotional time, but it is very upsetting for midwives who have taken time and patience to explain things to patients and partners and then receive a letter of complaint a few months later about staff attitudes.

Even in the antenatal period there are potential problems, it seems. The need to balance giving out information so as to enable informed decision making without inducing fear is a tightrope those involved in Parentcraft must walk.

I think we have been sadly lacking in helping to enlighten clients on the process, physiology and alternatives which may arise during their pregnancy and subsequent labours. The clients themselves are setting unrealistic goals. We ask them to make a birth plan; many go into detail which they have barely researched, and come up with what is their ideal plan. Unfortunately I have never yet seen a labour or delivery that went to plan. Childbirth to me is one of Nature's wonders and should be taken a step at a time. I know of one colleague who was censured for telling a Preparation for Parenthood class at a labour talk that they would experience excruciating pain. Is this the right approach? We leave ourselves wide open for criticism.

There is clearly a need for practitioners to be sensitive to the needs of patients, especially when something has gone wrong.

The next question asked about communication and rapport between doctor and midwife in the same circumstances. It will be seen that the doctors consistently had a higher opinion of such staff relationships than did the midwives (Fig 9.1).

Why midwives should be of the opinion that staff relationships are so much worse than doctors is not clear. Over half the midwives described such relationships at best as 'Fair' when things go wrong. Within the midwifery survey there were statistically significant differences in the Scottish-English matched pairs trial, with the English group more likely to answer 'Very Good/Good' both generally and when something has gone wrong.[1] There was correspondingly a statistically significant difference in the proportion answering either 'Poor' or 'Terrible' when something had gone wrong. These differences were not replicated in this obstetric survey.

Figure 9.1   How would you rate communication and rapport between doctors and midwives in your unit generally?

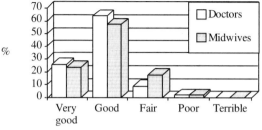

Figure 9.2   How would you rate communication and rapport between doctors and midwives in your unit when something has gone wrong?

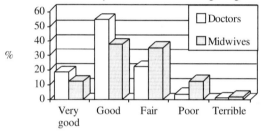

Table 9.3:

Scottish-English midwives' matched pairs: How would you rate communication and rapport between midwife and doctor in your unit

		Very good/good	Fair	Poor/terrible
generally	Eng	148	22	1
	Sco	124	41	5
when something has gone wrong	Eng	104	49	17
	Sco	69	65	35

This difference in the midwife-doctor relationship appears very stark. One explanation is the theory of a more imposing Scottish medical establishment, mentioned above in the section on home delivery, and referred to here by one midwife who has worked in both England and Scotland:

> I think Scotland's medical establishment does not recognize the potential of midwives and therefore we as a profession do not stand up against this due to fear of confrontation ...

1 These both reached statistical significance: respectively $p < .01$ and $p < .001$.

Experience in this area clearly varies, since a seventh of all respondents cited 'Poor/Terrible' for when things go wrong. The question did not specify obstetricians only, and one respondent, while mentioning obstetricians, also added this comment about other doctors.

> Communication between obstetricians and midwives is generally non-existent when problems arise. Paediatricians are too quick to blame the labour/delivery without really knowing about the details. I personally feel that in our unit they cause more problems because they are very quick to apportion blame to the midwives/obstetricians if a baby is ill or traumatized.

This doesn't sound like a unit where relationships are good; and midwives from several other units made similar comments.

> (Lack of respect by obstetricians for midwives) has all led to more antagonism between midwives and doctors and their respective roles leading to a lack of team work, witch hunting when things go wrong. We don't work together no matter how hard people say they try.

> Doctors dissociate themselves from midwives when something goes wrong.

> I feel that there is a gulf between medical staff and midwifery staff, where medical staff will never back midwives in the event of difficulties. I work constantly in fear of litigation from clients, and also from pressure form medical staff. I feel the attitude in my unit is 'Cover your back' at all times.

> There is widespread ignorance of the 'role' of the midwife, her accountability and the parameters of her practice. Most doctors see a 'supervisory' role for them over a midwife which is offensive in the extreme ...

There were also comments about how poor relationships can cause anguish.

> SHOs and registrars can be off putting when asked to see a client, and you are left to reassure client on what is happening, and left watching fetal distress until finally they do a LSCS.

For one respondent problems could occur according to the level of experience of the doctor.

> Better rapport between midwives and senior medical staff than with SHOs, especially if new to obstetrics – medical arrogance persisting in 'I'm doctor, you nurse' attitude – takes time to overcome this.

Once again there was the expressed feeling that doctors will close ranks in the event of something going wrong.

> One comment I must make is with regard to support which is received when something goes wrong (not necessarily resulting in litigation). Thankfully this has never happened to me, but I have been witness to seeing people after the event.

The difference between medical and midwifery staff was amazing. The medical staff tend to 'close ranks', and give the doctor the support he requires. Not so the midwife. It's as if there is something in-built, that we must find someone to blame, therefore the midwife is somewhat solitary.

Not all comments were completely adverse, however.

We are encouraged by managers to attend weekly meetings with the doctor – audit and perinatal. We discuss complimentary therapy with them – the doctors can be cynical but open to listening. On labour ward the doctors are supportive and if you say you don't want/need their involvement they will not enter the room at all.

We meet regularly with our consultant to discuss cases – very supportive – occasionally he can be arrogant/judgmental in his assessment, but he is approachable to challenge and eager that we challenge his ideas.

It is worrying that so many practitioners view these matters so pessimistically, for good staff relationships are essential for effective care. The question of staff morale within the health service has received considerable media publicity in recent years, and it may be that some of these views are expressions of a more general dissatisfaction. Whether or not this is the case, the high prevalence of staff who view workplace relationships in such a critical light must be a matter of concern for health service managers. 'Team-building' concepts are perhaps more familiar within industry, but it seems that there is a need for such an approach within maternity care – and especially within Scotland, if these answers are to be taken at face value.

Summary

- Communication and rapport between practitioner and patient are generally felt by both doctors and midwives to be good. There is a 'downward' shift in the perception of relationships when things are deemed to have gone wrong which is much more marked among midwives. To deal effectively with poor outcomes requires that attention be paid to this area, and there is room for a much more proactive response by clinicians in these situations.

- Almost all the doctors believed their working relationships with midwives on the whole to be good. However a significant proportion of midwives characterized such relationships in a less optimistic light, particularly when there has been a poor clinical outcome. In such circumstances over a third described relationships as only fair, with a further seventh describing them as either poor or terrible. There are clear implications for practitioners here, for if midwives and doctors cannot maintain good communications the prospects for effective communication with patients are seriously diminished.

CHAPTER TEN

Dealing with Poor Outcomes

Counselling procedures

Respondents were asked about formal counselling procedures for patients when there has been an adverse outcome to the pregnancy. The Birth Afterthoughts service mentioned in Chapter 9 is one example of such a procedure. Moves towards establishing counselling for patients has received some publicity, but it is unclear how prevalent or effective such facilities are. Crowther (1995) reports one study which found that over half the women who had had a previous stillbirth or neonatal death had a poor or confused knowledge of the events surrounding the death. That there is a clear need for this sort of approach was confirmed by the evidence of the RCOG in the Winteron Report: 'many medico-legal actions can be avoided by a full and frank discussion between the consultant concerned and the patient as soon as possible after the event' (House of Commons, 1992).

Sixty-two per cent of the midwives said there were formal procedures within their unit, indicating fairly widespread implementation; however this could be skewed by answers from the larger units (which did show a higher than average 'Yes' response). Least likely to say 'Yes' were those from the smaller units: 31% from units of up to 100 deliveries, and 46% from units with 100–999 deliveries. This is perhaps surprising, given the image of smaller units being less impersonal places. Almost two-thirds of doctors (63%) claimed their unit has such a facility, with a quarter (and half the GPs) saying it does not. Size of unit had no effect on answers.

However, knowledge of their existence in units where some doctors claimed they do exist was scarcely universal: in only four out of the remaining 28 units could all the respondents agree that such procedures were available. Even among consultants there was a surprising lack of agreement: in only ten out 24 units could all the consultants agree that such procedures exist.

The importance of counselling was stressed by several respondents.

> I have had a degree of interest in debriefing patients postnatally, sometimes up to three years later, when the woman is contemplating another pregnancy ... (in) most instances anxiety, unhappiness, and sheer terror of her experience has resulted from a doctor usually, but sometimes a midwife, failing to 'communicate', i.e. examined her or carried out a procedure without explanation or even introducing themselves ... in several instances the women feel that sheer rudeness has offended them and left them with very bad feelings about their experience.

> I have heard it said that the whole story only comes out in court. So hopefully more open and honest discussion with clients would reduce the incidence of litigation if clients feel they have (not) been given a full explanation.

A debrief session the day following delivery has helped a lot of women to clarify events which happened during their labour.

However not all appeared to feel that there is enough support. One who said there were counselling procedures in her unit added that they were 'very poor'. Another common complaint was that in many units there are no procedures for counselling staff involved either in legal action or in a clinical case which has had a poor outcome. A rather plaintive appeal from one midwife was 'Where is the counselling for staff?' Another commented:

No proper counselling from within Health Service for patients or staff (in obstetrics). Counselling usually available from voluntary organizations. Staff obtain support by discussing problems with each other. Very seldom any support from management.

This expression of a perceived gulf between midwives and managers was a recurring theme.

I do not feel midwives get enough support or counselling from their midwifery managers or charge nurses *(sic)*.

Generally there is distrust between midwives and managers.

This last comment relates back to the discussion above about complaints made about staff, and specifically how managers deal with these.

Management taking too heavy a hand in disciplinary procedures encouraging staff to be defensive and doubt their ability. Encourages poor morale.

The patient is always right, no matter what. Once a complaint is made the damage is done.

However it is not just managers who are criticized: some of the comments above have indicated a lack of team support, and this is echoed by the respondent who claims:

I do feel conscious that if there was personal litigation you would be pretty much on your own on an accountability level.

As autonomous practitioners each midwife must be prepared to be accountable for what she does (and does not do) in the course of her duty, but there appears to be a perception among some that should an individual be involved in litigation or a complaint then she would receive no support from colleagues at all. It is to be hoped that this would not be the case, but the statement made by one midwife personally involved in litigation, that 'I wanted to form a support group for midwives who had been in that position. I wanted to be there for them, because I felt no one was there for me' indicates that this may not be so.

The format of such procedures will vary from one unit to another; in medico-legal terms the emphasis is on answering questions openly and honestly in an attempt to avoid those legal claims which are made on the basis of a misunderstanding. Anaesthetists have instigated such review procedures for patients, especially those who have had an epidural or spinal anaesthetic. Given that events during caesarean section are frequently the subject of complaints and claims, such procedures by obstetricians may also be beneficial. Perinatal outcomes analysis, which has been introduced in at least one area which formed part of this survey, aims to identify all poor outcomes, and initiate a full examination to establish whether the outcome was preventable and if so, which staff may be involved in subsequent investigations. This management of potential claims endeavours to shorten and simplify the huge task of investigating events which occurred perhaps several years ago, it not being uncommon for claims to take several years to come to light. With all the staff involved clearly identified, and with these staff all making full records of what happened, when and why, the decision whether or not to defend a claim can be made much more easily. In theory this will reduce legal costs, lessen the stress of retrospective investigation on staff, and ensure quicker compensation for those patients who have a genuine case.

Complaints

The level of complaints, anecdotally, is increasing; and certainly more complaints are being referred to the Ombudsman: Warden (1996) notes a 28% increase in the yearly figures for 1994–95. One area which may predispose towards instigating complaints or even litigation is the perception by patients of staff attitudes. The next question asked whether a patient had ever complained in such a way, firstly in relation to the respondent personally, and secondly with regard to any of his/her colleagues. One doctor commented:

> It would be unrealistic to expect there never to be even the slightest disagreement between staff and patients. Fortunately in our unit for me personally this is exceedingly rare.

Although it may seem as if there is a natural progression from initial complaint to more formal action, it is claimed that the majority of complaints are not pursued rigorously; nevertheless, to obviate complacency, we should find out more about them (Lamont, 1993).

However, as Whelan (1988) points out, 'complaints procedures are effective if they provide incentives to take a proper degree of care'. Neuberger points out that very often patients do not want to go through complicated or formal proceedings, but are anxious 'to get some form of apology and expression of concern'. She goes on to add that the medical defence organisations 'have been fairly negative about expressing apologies on the basis that they could, in fact, consist of being an admission of liability of some kind' (cited in Wall, 1991). From personal data I know this to have happened on occasion. One Consultant wrote in some exasperation to a senior hospital official:

> I apologized to (the patient) because in a mature and understanding world it is proper to express regret to any patient who considers that she has had a difficult time. That apology is not of negligence, it is of understanding and good manners, and let us hope that type of relationship never be lost in this litigation conscious world.

Clearly practitioners have to tread warily for fear of encouraging the perception that negligence has occurred. Nevertheless complaints must be dealt with sensitively: a reluctance to give a full and frank reply may be seen by some as evidence of a cover up.

Forty-one per cent of doctors admitted that they had been the subject of a complaint at some time, and the senior grades were much more likely to be in this group. Analysis by length of experience showed those who had not had a complaint made against them to have an average of 11.9 years in obstetrics; those with a complaint 15.7 years. The English doctors were also more likely to say they had been the subject of a complaint: 62% compared with 41% of the Scottish hospital based staff; only 17% of GPs had received such a complaint. A large majority of doctors (87%) knew of a colleague who had been the recipient of a complaint; all of the English staff were in this group.

Of the 1,767 midwives who answered, 294 (17%) admitted that they had been the subject of such a complaint. More likely to be in this group were those of a higher grade (including nine of the 35 lecturers). There was clearly some association between this and length of experience; and again, those in larger units were more likely to be included. How these complaints were handled sometimes caused distress.

> I was an RCM steward for 12 years. I found that in the last eight years my manager would go immediately into a 'disciplinary' mode with midwives immediately a complaint was made. The midwives felt that they were being unjustly accused by the manager and that the complainants were automatically in the right and that they were automatically at fault. This caused very low morale in the unit as the midwives felt they were not being supported by the management, and this affected their practice in that they lost confidence.

While a sixth of the midwives had said they had themselves been the subject of a complaint, a large majority (85%) knew of someone else who had. Perhaps surprisingly, those longest qualified (above 12 years) were less likely to say this than those qualified less than 12 years. Size of unit showed no association, except for those in the smallest units, who were much less likely (at 66%) to say they knew of a colleague involved in such a complaint.

It has been noted above that some respondents feel that when a complaint is made, midwifery and administrative managers are all too ready to believe that the very existence of the complaint means that the practitioner is guilty. Comments like 'In a court of law you are innocent until proven guilty. With the NHS it's the opposite', and 'I feel both midwifery and hospital managers want staff to submit statements about complaints without referring them first to the RCM rep.' make this point very forcefully. On the latter claim, practitioners are strongly advised not to write reports quickly or 'under duress' (Brown, 1990). Truelove (1985) warns that taking complaints at face value can be misleading. Some complaints are understated, and so may not be sufficiently investigated; equally misleading is to assume that if the person is unreasonable, the complaint must be unreasonable.

One midwifery manager told me that complaints were once rare, but were now coming in 'like confetti'. Such a situation can be taken as indicating that women have lost their trust in the medical and midwifery professions, a claim made by Beech (1986). Very few doctors (10%) agreed with this, but the English-based staff were much more of this view (28% compared with 9%). No GPs agreed. The respondent's grade and size of unit did not appear to affect answers. One SHO who disagreed added:

They are just more hesitant in placing their trust and quicker to question.

Very few midwives (131 – 7%) either agreed or strongly agreed; 377 (21%) were non-committal; 1,104 (63%) disagreed, and 151 (9%) strongly disagreed. Those qualified less than nine years were more likely to agree, as were those in the smallest units (less than 100 deliveries a year). One who strongly agreed added ' + + + ' to show her strength of feeling about this. Another who agreed added '20–30%'. One summed up her reasons for feeling that staff almost deserve this diminishing trust.

With the growing hypothetical Patients' rights – these rights often being over staff – then they have no confidence in us, because we are no longer united, we are all back stabbing to appear the nicest professional towards the patients; it's like a popularity competition. The end of the day patients would respect and have more trust in staff who are united and stop blaming each other ... the staff would be more confident and make better decisions as the fear of litigation would be greatly reduced.

Several divided their answers, ticking 'Agree' for medical staff, but 'Disagree' for midwives. One described the situation in her area:

A minority of women distrust the medical profession, and the general public is unaware largely of the skills of the midwife. Women in this area tend to be fairly conservative and not particularly well informed, and consequently quite willing for professionals to take control.

Did the midwives feel that in the last ten years there has been a 'breakdown of trust between providers and patients' (Dingwall, 1986)? While only 7% of the midwives had agreed with the statement that women have lost their trust with the medical and midwifery professions, 19% thought there had been a breakdown of trust; 1,202 (68%) answered 'No' to this, with 234 (13%) unsure. By grade most likely to say 'Yes' were the I grades, with 10 out of 22 agreeing. Length of experience showed no direct association, although a small difference was noted between those qualified less than 12 years, and those qualified more, the former group being slightly more likely to say 'Yes' than the latter. Size of unit showed no strong variation.

There were many comments added to this question; they included:

I think a certain social group may have lost this trust because of pressure from 'strong' unprofessional groups and their misconceptions about midwifery practice. Once these things are explained to patients they understand why certain procedures may have to be carried out.

I think people want to trust the people looking after them in labour, and an opportunity to build a relationship with a midwife before labour would be welcome by most women. If things go wrong people want explanations and apologies and are entitled to that.

I feel that clients have good faith and trust in midwives but are not always informed of care available and choices they can make.

Generally there is distrust between midwives and managers.

Not a breakdown, but a weakening, definitely.

I would question if breakdown in trust has occurred in last ten years, but feel that women are more likely to express distrust and choose alternative methods of care, because we are now more open to provide them. They probably always had a distrust, especially following a bad outcome.

One who answered 'No' added 'If anything this must be improving!' Although most of the comments attached to this question were from those agreeing, it should be stressed that many more respondents disagreed.

Cooperation with consumer groups

The next question asked whether there was cooperation in the respondent's area between providers of maternity services and consumer/user groups. As Durward and Evans (1990) note, there has been a burgeoning of pressure and self-help groups in recent years, although Edwards (1996) points out that the presence of representatives from such groups on Maternity Services Liaison Committees is no guarantee that their views will be accorded much weight.

Consumer groups may be the first point of contact for someone who feels she has had a less than optimal outcome to her pregnancy and who wishes to make a complaint. The relationship between such groups and health providers is therefore critical, and given the vaunted openness of the new health service it might be assumed that cooperation was endemic. Answers are as shown.

Table 10.1:
Midwives: Do you believe there is cooperation between providers of maternity care in your area and user groups/consumer groups?

	Often	*Occasionally*	*Rarely*	*Never*
n =	675	854	178	12
%	39	50	10	0.7

There was a significant difference in responses according to length of experience, with an increasing propensity among the more experienced to say 'Often'.

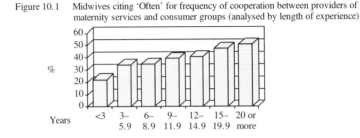

Figure 10.1 Midwives citing 'Often' for frequency of cooperation between providers of maternity services and consumer groups (analysed by length of experience)

This may simply reflect the likelihood that contact with consumer groups comes with increased experience. Those working in the smaller units (less than 1,000 deliveries) were more likely to say 'Often', with those in the medium sized units (1,000–3,999 deliveries) least likely to. The association with size of unit was not direct, since those in units of 4,000 deliveries or above were more likely to say 'Often' than those in the medium size units. One respondent who answered 'Never' added 'Opinionated consultants' as her perception of why that should be so.

These answers are unlikely to find much favour with those consumer groups which advocate minimal intervention. The relationships between maternity care providers and those who organize support and advice for pregnant women is often rather a fraught one, anecdotally at least. The following question asked whether consumer group material was allowed in the respondent's unit – a sign of some degree of cooperation. Consumer group material is usually targeted at antenatal clinic and ward areas, where, in theory, women have some time on their hands, and may be motivated to pick up leaflets and information packs.

Most doctors (57%) claimed that such literature is available in their unit, with junior staff less likely to be included in this. A small number (6%) said it is not available, and rather worryingly 36% said they did not know whether it is. While junior members of staff, perhaps new to a unit, may not be expected to know for sure, almost a quarter of consultants did not know either. The English doctors were more likely to say it is available: 75% compared with 55%.

Most midwives (73%) said that consumer group material was allowed into their unit, with only 8% saying it wasn't; 19% weren't sure (3 of the 8 managers came into this category). Length of experience appeared to affect answers to a degree, with those qualified less than six years less likely to say 'Yes' than those qualified for longer. Analysis by size of unit showed very little variation. The most commonly cited groups are shown here, although bald figures mean little without knowing how many units allow this material in; since the questionnaire did not ask the respondent to identify her unit, these figures should be interpreted with some caution.

Those who said the literature was available were asked to stipulate which groups were included.

Table 10.2:

Consumer groups allowed to publicize themselves in the respondent's unit

Cited by doctors	n =	Cited by midwives	n =
National Childbirth Trust	59	National Childbirth Trust	937
SANDS	22	La Leche League	291
AIMS	9	SANDS	280
Miscarriage Association	4	TAMBA	108
La Leche League	4	Breastfeeding support	86
		AIMS	69

The number of citations can be misleading; at least one doctor from most units was able to cite at least one group, but this was not the case in five separate units (one a GP practice, two small DGHs, and two moderate sized DGHs).

The NCT are by far the most commonly cited, but as stated the number of different units is not known. One midwife who cited the NCT added: 'Token – only to sell bras!!', indicating that the presence of material may not be a reliable sign that cooperation exists. Some respondents had what might be seen as an ambivalent attitude towards some of the consumer groups.

> Far too much inaccurate info taught at NCT, AIMS groups etc. Should be more closely monitored. A lot of these people are not qualified to give such info. Would doctors, lawyers or other such professional bodies put up with such inaccurate bending and manipulation of their good name – I don't think so.

> It is very easy to jump on a few rare incidents and blow them up out of all proportion.

Under reasons for an increase in litigation (see Chapter 2), there were comments such as:

> Peer group pressure; lay groups e.g. NCT, AIMS.

> Women reading and listening to the NCT.

It seems that there is still much ground to be made up before cooperation can be said to exist. Some midwives certainly seemed to feel that the consumer groups did not understand the strains of the job, and it may equally be said that consumer groups may feel their message has been poorly understood by some midwives, not to mention obstetricians.

Summary

- Cooperation between hospitals/practitioners and user groups/consumer groups was popularly held by midwives to happen at least occasionally, if not often; nevertheless a tenth claimed that this occurs either rarely or not at all. Despite the supposed openness of the health service today, there remains room for improvement in this area.

- 17% of midwives and 41% of doctors admitted that they had been the subject of a complaint by a patient, and a large majority of both groups knew of a colleague in such a position. Complaints are said to be much more frequent, especially since the Patients' Charter (and similar local initiatives) which advertize the right of patients to lodge complaints. Whether such a rise in complaints also indicates a rise in formal litigation is not clear, but is being examined by this researcher.

- A common complaint by midwives was that managers are seen to provide inadequate support, especially in times of stress. It was alleged that complaints are often taken at face value, with guilt on the part of staff members automatically assumed. Support generally for midwives involved in legal cases would seem at times to be inadequate.

- Formal review procedures for patients who have suffered a poor outcome were believed by a majority of the doctors to be in existence, although there was little unanimity in opinion about this between practitioners from the same unit.

CHAPTER ELEVEN

Summary and Discussion

This chapter summarizes and discusses the principal findings of this research, and places them in the context of certain other research findings concerning legal matters and obstetric and midwifery practice. In no way is this intended to be the definitive version of such a complex subject. However it is hoped that this discussion will shed some light on certain claims made in the literature, and highlight areas which deserve further investigation.

The survey targeted a large number of midwives and obstetricians in Scotland and in two identified English areas. When the questionnaire was formulated, comprehensive information about the nature of litigation was not available, although certain aspects were highlighted in the literature. The questions reflected many of these issues, such as clinical decisions, choice, consent, and communication. While some areas (such as supervision and CTG monitoring) have been seen in the parallel analysis of legal files to have a direct bearing on actual legal cases (Symon, 1997b, 1997c), others, such as the question of home versus hospital delivery, are more tangential.

In all, over 2,000 practitioners responded to this survey. Details about the respondents can be found in Appendices A and B. With a 63% return rate, reasonable reliability about obstetricians' attitudes in these areas can be assumed, for the Scottish-based obstetricians at least. The English subsample was small and the views of these respondents may not be typical. The survey targeted all full RCM members in Scotland, and used RCM membership to target midwives in one of the two identified English areas; for the other English area the hospital management supplied a coded list of midwives. The 51% return rate for the midwifery questionnaire (after one postal reminder) was less than ideal, but is apparently reasonable in terms of getting midwives to reply to postal surveys. The scale of the survey means that, while a larger return rate would have been desirable, the sample is very large, and a considerable range of views was still obtained. I believe that reasonable reliability can be assumed for the Scottish respondents. While the English-based sub-sample was smaller, it still comprised 231 respondents, and there is no particular reason to feel that they were not typical of English midwives generally. The midwifery matched pairs trial, with 172 matched pairs, allowed for Scottish and English responses to be compared directly. Unfortunately the English obstetric subsample was too small to allow for a matched pairs trial in the obstetric survey.

The scale of litigation

Even a casual search of the literature on medical negligence litigation will find an almost universal belief that litigation has been increasing for some time. Some of these claims were discussed in Chapter 1, and it is not proposed to go over this ground again, except to say that most of the claims made have been based on relatively small-scale studies. Given this received wisdom, however, it was no great surprise to find that a large majority of both doctors (90%) and midwives (86%) in this survey believed litigation in obstetrics/midwifery has increased over the last ten years. While my own research confirms that overall numbers are up, the recent drop in both rate and incidence of litigation, in both Scotland as a whole and in two of the three English hospitals studied, was not something of which any of the respondents appeared to be aware. This is hardly surprising, since little in the way of such statistics are ever published.

Why people sue is another area which has received some speculation, though little detailed analysis. Interestingly the recent Audit Commission (1997) report only mentions litigation with reference to the increasing caesarean section rate, and there is no doubt from this research that this is a factor. In this research respondents largely ascribed the apparent increase in litigation to rising expectations and awareness on the part of the public generally, and of patients specifically.

Whereas few midwives had been personally involved in legal actions relating to alleged negligence, almost half the obstetricians had been involved at least once or twice, and 13% had been involved at least three times. While it was clear that litigation is seen by most as a threat, there were a few who felt it to have positive aspects too. The view was expressed that having to deal with the possibility of litigation meant that midwives had started to develop support systems to cope with the stresses and responsibilities of their role, and that the way information is given to patients is now much more sensitive (and hopefully effective). Whether this is so can only be assessed by local audit initiatives. It is important for health service providers to be aware of any deficiencies in this regard.

A third of those doctors who thought litigation had not increased, or who were unsure, had themselves been involved, yet almost half of those who thought litigation *had* increased had not themselves been personally involved. Perceptions about this issue cannot be put down to personal experience alone. The lack of comprehensive data in the literature means that few practitioners have accurate information about either the scale or nature of litigation.

All of the English doctors agreed that litigation has increased, and they were much more likely to discuss both personal involvement and the possibility of being sued than their Scottish counterparts; 65% of the English doctors had been involved in litigation compared to 52% of the Scottish hospital doctors (and only 11% of the GPs). The rate of litigation fell in two of the three English hospitals under review in the parallel research, in line with the overall fall in Scotland, so while the true rate may be different in the two countries, the overall pattern appears to be similar.

For obstetricians increasing length of experience was positively associated with legal involvement; initially this may suggest that an obstetrician will become involved if only he/she is clinically involved for long enough. However, analysis of the consultants' responses (they were the group most often involved in legal actions) showed this not to be the case: those consultants who had never been involved, or who had been involved only once or twice, had practised for just as long as those who were involved more often. They also worked in units of comparable size, and undertook almost as many deliveries. Involvement in litigation among midwives was not positively associated with length of experience, size of unit, or area of work.

It may be concluded that litigation is a relatively haphazard affair. This is not to suggest that it can never be predicted (poor standards of care will always predispose to it), only that there are many variables which must be taken into account, including possible reasons for suing (and for not suing). It cannot be concluded that the initiation of a legal action indicates the presence of negligence; nor, by the same measure, does the absence of litigation necessarily indicate patient satisfaction. Given that a minority of medical negligence actions succeed, the fact that a midwife or obstetrician has been accused of negligence does not necessarily make them a bad practitioner, although it will almost certainly make them a stressed practitioner. Vincent et al (1994b) note the detrimental effect of litigation on clinicians, an area which must be tackled at local level by the development of support systems. From the midwives' responses in particular, there would appear to be considerable room for improvement in helping practitioners to cope with the stress of litigation.

Defensiveness

The imprecision of this subject has already been discussed in Chapter 4. What one practitioner considers to be defensive will be seen by another as good sound clinical practice. Simanowitz (1989) claims that 'the issue of "defensive obstetrics" is one of propaganda ... as long as health professionals stick to ... guidelines ... namely that the only action taken must be clinically justified, they will not be at risk of litigation.' Two criticisms of this view may be offered. First it assumes that all practitioners will view a given situation in the same light and apply objective clinical guidelines, when in fact much health care can be thought of as more 'art' than 'science', and so not subject to a definitive and objective view. The differences in opinion noted in CTG interpretation, even when the same person views the same trace twice (Nielsen et al, 1987), is evidence of this. Secondly it overstates the protection which following clinical guidelines offers: doing so may make it unlikely that a plaintiff/pursuer will sue *successfully*, but it will not deter every dissatisfied patient from initiating a legal action. The low success rate of medical negligence litigation bears testimony to this.

The research highlighted an interesting division in perceptions concerning the prevalence of defensive practice. A large majority of respondents believed litigation had increased, and yet less than half the doctors (and only just over half the midwives) said they had changed their clinical practice as a result of the fear of litigation. Nevertheless a greater proportion of each group thought that clinical practice generally is becoming defensive. That many practitioners believe – and assert – that such defensiveness exists was confirmed in the Winterton report: 'It is clear that professionals' practice is influenced by their fear of litigation ...' (House of Commons, 1992). The English doctors generally were much more likely to say they had changed practice in some way (76% compared with 42% of Scottish hospital doctors). It does seem, at least from this survey, that litigation awareness (as measured by discussing legal matters and altering practice to try and avoid legal entanglement) is much higher in England.

For doctors the most commonly cited example both of altering personal practice, and of a belief in obstetric practice generally becoming defensive, was an increase in the number of caesarean sections, a fear reported in the Audit Commission (1997) report. This reflects the very natural fear of being accused of not proceeding quickly enough (or at all) to caesarean section in the presence of either fetal acidosis or a recognized and serious fetal heart rate abnormality. Measures to reduce the caesarean section rate have been instigated, but these will have to fight against the public's assumed causal connection between intrapartum events and brain damage. Doctors in this survey were on the whole aware of the probability of a causal relationship between intrapartum events and cerebral palsy. Midwives were much less aware, and there is a need to improve this perception amongst midwives if the public's apparent misperception is to be corrected.

The most commonly cited instance of changing personal practice among the midwives was an improvement in documentation; this was cited by 41% of all respondents. This is a difficult area to quantify: much has been written on the need for thorough and accurate documentation, not least to avoid medico-legal pitfalls (Dornan, 1990; Rosenberger, 1995), but the literature reveals no studies assessing the quality of record keeping. It is one area, however, which may be amenable to audit (Hughes and Goldstone, 1989). Other examples of a change in practice among midwives included obtaining permission for all procedures, and involving doctors more quickly. While the first is surely a good thing, the second is more debatable. If done unnecessarily, this may simply increase the risk of intervention and consequent morbidity, which may itself lead to increased dissatisfaction. Such unnecessary referrals can be overcome with increased experience and confidence, and with a mutual respect and understanding between doctors and midwives of each other's role.

Doctors on the whole believed obstetrics generally to be becoming defensive: even 65% of those who said they had not changed their own clinical practice believed this. Again this perception was more common amongst the English respondents (90% compared with 78% of the Scottish hospital doctors). English midwives were also much more likely to be of this view. Far fewer GPs agreed, however. It is difficult to determine exactly how much and in what ways individuals are tailoring their clinical practice to deal with the fear of litigation. One respondent warned of the dangers of being too bound by this fear, claiming that many younger midwives now appear unable to make decisions without considering the possible legal consequences; this makes them less decisive, and more likely to defer to medical staff which diminishes their midwifery role to the extent that they become 'maternity nurses'. Few would wish to see this situation develop, but how midwives can enhance their responsibilities and sphere of practice without encountering a need on the part of employers to feel protected (often through establishing protocols and policies) remains a thorny issue. The definition of a midwife as an 'autonomous practitioner' looks a little optimistic viewed against the apparent mushrooming of such protocols, which inevitably constrain personal preference and practice to a degree. Some may argue that this may ensure a more equal service, but whether or not such restrictions necessarily improve safety or satisfaction is very much open to question. With regard to safety, the Confidential Enquiry into Maternal Deaths (UK Health Departments, 1996) criticized the lack of guidelines for the immediate management of acute emergencies.

Further examples by respondents of defensive practice were more investigations (e.g. scans and CTGs) being carried out, and quicker interventions. Once more these views were shared by both midwives and obstetricians. Again, it is a debatable point whether such interventions actually improve overall outcomes. Given a traditional reluctance on the part of hospitals to publish their intervention rates (Waterson, 1993), obtaining comparable and comprehensive data is unlikely, and so monitoring of the effectiveness of such procedures must be carried out at local level.

The levels of stress which some feel, and the concerns about changes in current practice, were evident from many of the comments. One midwife said that she was alarmed by several of her younger colleagues claiming that they wished they'd chosen another profession; another, concerned at the fragmentation of the service, said she'd left midwifery practice and returned to general nursing. A third, on returning to midwifery part time after an absence, found she was scared by the level of litigation awareness amongst midwives, and felt that common sense was being excluded by the concern to document everything. Each situation will have its own characteristics, and it is impossible to generalize from these; nevertheless, managers may care to reflect that many staff apparently feel the support they receive from their manager/supervisor, particularly in times of stress, is inadequate.

Eleven of the doctors (5%) said they had considered leaving the speciality because of the fear of litigation, and 57 (a further 27%) knew of a colleague who had considered this. A similar proportion of midwives (5% and 22% respectively) claimed the same. Eight of the doctors who had considered leaving were consultants, the other three being a registrar, a staff grade, and one SHO.

While it is presumed that all of the midwives who had considered leaving clinical practice – still being full members of the RCM and citing a place of work – have not left (although one noted above had returned to general nursing), it is not known how many midwives may have already left practice, and whether litigation was a reason (or perhaps one of several). While this fear of litigation may be at a higher level than is warranted by actual occurrence or personal experience, this does not reduce the importance or effect of the fear. I hope the respondent who claimed that the possible repercussions scared her to death was exaggerating her case. Another pointed out that if practitioners were to worry constantly about litigation they would be unable to function effectively.

Considering leaving and actually leaving may be miles apart, but the fact that so many practitioners are even considering this is a matter for concern: disenchanted or frightened clinicians may not be as committed to their work. This feature of legal side effects may be countered to a degree by continuing education: if a clinician's practice can be judged as safe and competent by a body of co-professionals, there is nothing to fear in terms of being found to have acted negligently, as the law currently stands. This of course cannot preclude a dissatisfied patient taking legal advice and pursuing a course of legal action which will never succeed but which can cause immense damage en route. Education of the public about what may be clinical mistakes and what may simply be known complications of a procedure could help to reduce the large number of legal claims which are made without any real chance of success. This of course relates to communication and counselling, which are considered below.

Defensiveness is an imprecise concept. One practitioner's defensiveness is another's good sound clinical practice. Although almost impossible to define objectively, local monitoring of possible examples (such as increasing caesarean or forceps delivery rates, or CTG use) is essential. Responses of staff to the actual or perceived threat of litigation inevitably vary, but managers must be aware that some practitioners feel under considerable pressure. Whether the response on an individual or aggregate level can be said to be justified is debatable, but is something of which managers must be aware.

Perceived reasons for litigation

As noted above, an increase in expectations and awareness was held to be responsible for the perceived increase in litigation, and there is some evidence that this is not confined to medical matters. Architects and veterinary surgeons have also reported rapidly increasing levels of litigation (Ham et al, 1988). 'The most likely explanation', they say, is 'the awareness among victims of the possibility of legal redress and their readiness to pursue this route' (*ibid.*).

Some respondents expressed dissatisfaction stemming from changes within the National Health Service. Trust status, reduced staffing levels, and especially contemporary budget implications, were held responsible by a number of respondents for declining standards in patient care and subsequent litigation. Staff morale was also held to be lowered by all of these factors, which in turn increases sickness rates which then compounds the problem of poor staffing levels.

'The media' came in for some criticism both for its perceived tendency to raise expectations among the public and for its lurid and sensationalist reporting of a handful of probably atypical cases. Certainly the media has a significant role to play in educating pregnant women. The concern is that, in the interests of selling newspapers or obtaining high viewing figures, either the truth will be distorted or isolated instances used to portray rare occurrences as commonplace. The possibility that people may get paid large sums of money for their story also alarms some practitioners, as there may be a temptation to exaggerate in order to make the story more dramatic.

Some respondents cited the 'American influence' as a cause for increasing litigation here, and this seems to be a popularly held view. One referred to litigation as 'the American (Greed) disease', and another cited 'the American culture of suing'. Concern has been expressed that Britain is becoming a more litigious society, with people less likely to accept situations they find unsatisfactory, and the 'lottery culture', with the possibility of large payouts by the courts, has helped to encourage this. One midwife who has worked in both North America and Britain said she saw litigation consciousness increasing here, although she felt it not to be an overriding issue yet.

While it is true that there are some similarities between the American medico-legal system and that which operates in Britain, there are also sufficient differences which mean that the American 'crisis' is unlikely to be replicated here, at least in whole. The establishment of negligence is fault-based in both systems, but the distinctions introduced by a fee-paying medical model mean that the American situation can be described as a crisis of malpractice insurance rather than a crisis of malpractice itself. In the USA juries sit in judgement in medical negligence cases, and also decide the amount of damages – an invitation to lawyers to make their claims theatrical and emotional, which must be especially tempting when there is a brain damaged child to parade before the jury. In the USA contingency fees, where an agreed percentage of any damages are payable to the lawyer, are the norm: this has not been allowed in British courts.

Prospects for change

The situation in the USA has led some states to adopt carefully defined no-fault compensation systems, but the former Conservative government made it clear that it had no intention of doing anything similar here. The closest it came towards reform of the present arrangements was to set up the possibility of arbitration panels in a bid to avoid the antagonisms which occur in an adversarial legal system (DoH, 1991), and to commission a report by Lord Woolf into the civil justice system in England and Wales. His report has recommended mediation, possible arbitration, the speeding up of the legal process so that smaller claims are dealt with more efficiently, and case management by judges (Woolf, 1996). However, these do not answer the fundamental criticisms of the tort/delict process.

One of the criticisms is that there is comparatively little publicity in cases of obvious gross negligence, in which the defending authority will settle the action speedily. By contrast, in cases where the question of negligence is debatable or where a clinician's error has been marginal or has occurred in particularly difficult circumstances (such as very poor staffing levels), a practitioner is much more likely to end up in the glare of publicity as a messy court case examines all the arguments (Genn and Lloyd-Bostock, 1990). A further anomaly of the fault based system is that the amount of damages awarded when negligence is proved or admitted will reflect the severity of the consequences rather than the degree of negligence involved.

No-fault compensation

Most doctors said they would prefer obstetrics to be covered by a no-fault scheme for compensation. This reflects BMA policy, but realistically this appears unlikely in the near future. Two private member's bills advocating no-fault compensation (Harriet

Harman's in 1990; Rosie Barnes' in 1991) failed to gain sufficient parliamentary support, one of the main criticisms being the supposed cost of such a scheme. While such a scheme would assuredly reduce tensions within the delivery room between staff members, the question of accountability would remain, and this has been the sticking point for at least one consumer group (Simanowitz, 1987).

The RCM has considered no-fault compensation, and a strong case was made for this at the Branch Delegates' Meeting at the Annual General Meeting in 1989, but to date it has no policy position advocating a no-fault scheme. Some midwives argued for the introduction of a no-fault system, such as operates in Sweden and New Zealand. This argument is superficially attractive, since it appears to solve the problems of the fault-based system. However, as noted in Chapter 2, the Swedish and New Zealand schemes may be criticized on a number of grounds, including a lack of the predictability of decisions, and expense.

The principle behind no-fault is in fact rather more complex than it might at first seem. If 'need' were to replace 'fault' as the basis for compensation, the argument would then turn to the rationale for distinguishing a disability which is caused by a medical accident from one which simply results from the disease process. Extending the argument, Stapleton (1994) questions why the disabled should be treated preferentially over victims of other misfortunes. Noting that there is a long legal tradition which requires that the victims of negligently-caused accidents be compensated, Mansell (1997) points out that 'In tort a single tortfeasor (wrongdoer) is called upon to make good the damage, and clearly the losses of those disabled otherwise are not similarly individually attributable ... there is no long tradition of such compensation for those who have become ill.'

In trying to make out a pragmatic rationale for no-fault compensation, Brahams (1988) asks why a no-fault scheme should be restricted to medical accidents: 'Accepting that we cannot change the whole world at once, then why not start with injured patients?' Atiyah and Cane (1993) note that preferential treatment such as this is not necessarily wrong; but its proponents must be prepared to justify the reasons for making such distinctions. They claim that 'the only way of eliminating causal issues entirely is to base entitlement to compensation solely on the need of the plaintiff for compensation' (Atiyah and Cane, 1993). However, the political background must be taken into account: it seems unlikely that the Labour Government elected in Britain in 1997 will increase levels of public expenditure in order to provide a significant boost for victims of medical accidents.

Other possible reforms of current methods are to phase out lump sum damages payments and introduce structured settlements – an important point for defences to consider when making an offer or conceding liability in court. A lump sum payment may be based on an anticipated lifespan of sixty or seventy years, whereas the child (or adult) in question may live only a few years after the case is settled. Structured settlements have sometimes been used in Britain, but this is not yet the norm, and the failure to do this has caused problems. In one recent case (Calladine v Nottingham AHA [unreported]) a child with cerebral palsy unexpectedly died just a week after her parents were awarded £700,000 by the High Court. Following the child's death, the Health Authority announced that it would appeal against the settlement (Anon, 1997b). Brahams (1988) notes that in the Finnish drug and patient insurance schemes (based on the Swedish model) payments are by instalment and not lump sum, so that 'the family of a compensated victim do not gain by his untimely death.'

A new litigation authority (the Clinical Negligence Scheme for Trusts – CNST) has been set up which aims to simplify the claims process in England. However, this only rearranges how the health service deals with a fault-based system which requires that compensation be paid when negligence and ensuing damage are established.

This whole debate is one which sometimes engenders as much heat as light, and undoubtedly the arguments both for and against reform will continue to be made. There is a need for a clear understanding of the strengths and weaknesses of the current system if fundamental changes are to be implemented, as many of the respondents in this research desire.

A change which, if it comes, will be unwelcome to many health service personnel, is a move to limit the applicability of the Bolam principle in English law. The Bolam approach is sometimes characterized unflatteringly as 'The doctor's friend', the argument being that if a doctor (or other healthcare professional) can find colleagues who are deemed to be responsible to say that they would have acted in the same way, then negligence cannot be established. The proposed change was advocated by one (dissenting) judge in a recent Court of Appeal case[1] (which subsequently went to the House of Lords): he distinguished applying the Bolam principle to the standard of care criterion, and applying it to the question of causation. This approach, if it ever becomes standard, would give considerable leeway to the courts to disregard the evidence brought on behalf of a defendant/defender, and is a prospect which some lawyers clearly relish. Goldrein (1994) claims it is surprising that the courts have allowed the medical profession to retain this sovereignty over evidence when they (the courts) have jealously asserted their rights to determine such matters in other fields. At present this new line has not been adopted by the courts, but moves to circumscribe the privileged position of medical expert witnesses may be seen as a worrying development.

Causes of dissatisfaction

Many midwives commented on the 'rights' given by the Patients' Charter, and several bemoaned the fact that there is no Charter to protect staff. In some cases it appears that litigation is the focus for people's antagonisms which stem from a number of different areas. These included staffing levels, with the view expressed that improving these would improve relationships and so help reduce litigation. Also commented on were the effects that non-clinical requirements (such as administrative work and the teaching of students) have on the standard of care which midwives are able to give.

---

1 Bolitho v City & Hackney HA 4 Med LR [1993] 381

Invasive obstetric technology is a subject which divides many commentators. Intended to ensure (as much as is possible) a live mother and the safe delivery of a healthy infant, many aspects of it have been criticized for leading to unnecessary intervention and for unfairly claiming the credit for improved perinatal outcomes. Such a cause of potential dissatisfaction needs to be addressed, especially in the light of the criticisms of the Winterton Report (House of Commons, 1992) which highlighted the potential for a demarcation dispute between doctors and midwives over the most appropriate approach for the supervision of women in labour.

Almost a fifth of doctors agreed that the level of such technology is too high within their own unit, and almost a third felt this to be true of Britain as a whole. Respondents from the larger units were more likely to answer this way; length of experience mattered little. Midwives were much more likely to feel that such technology is at a too high level, both within their own units (32%), and in Britain generally (46%). The most commonly cited examples by doctors of this were CTG use, caesarean section, and induction of labour.

A point made strongly by many midwives was that while on the one hand some consumer groups are claiming there ought to be less in the way of intervention in pregnancy and labour, many such procedures and even operations are performed at the request of the patient. Clinicians face a difficult choice in advising a patient of the suitability or otherwise of a procedure such as induction of labour when the patient herself demands that it be carried out. Inappropriate induction can lead to an increased level of intervention and need for analgesia, and to lowered satisfaction on the part of the patient who may herself have requested it. How clinicians react to such requests will of course vary; but the possibility that they will in fact lead to a poorer outcome and consequent resentment must be borne in mind.

This is of course only a snapshot of potential causes of dissatisfaction. Many Trusts now routinely survey the views of patients in an effort to identify areas where improvements can be made. Staff need to be 'on board' in such exercises, however: many midwives believed that criticisms of practitioners are taken at face value, with staff assumed to be at fault. This decreased the level of trust and confidence in their managers, and further lowered morale levels. If surveying the views of patients in an attempt to improve standards is deemed to be worthwhile, perhaps similar initiatives concerning the views of staff might be implemented.

Supervision

The report on Confidential Enquiries into Maternal Deaths (UK Health Departments, 1996) concluded that some deaths in hospital were due to 'too much responsibility (being) taken by, or ... delegated to, inexperienced staff'. How staff become experienced enough to deal with emergencies is of course complex: the Confidential Enquiry into Stillbirths and Deaths in Infancy (MCHRC, 1997) recommended the development of methods to determine how the accreditation of skills is achieved. While the aim of obstetric care is to minimize maternal and perinatal mortality, use of these criteria as outcome measures may be criticized: overall numbers are thankfully low, and although large variations exist between different areas 'the differences are not statistically significant and are most likely to be due to chance' (ISD, 1996).

However, inadequate supervision of patients and junior staff has been identified as a factor not only in those cases which are included in mortality statistics, but in a range of suboptimal outcomes, and is a described feature of perinatal litigation (Ennis and Vincent, 1990). In a survey of obstetric SHOs, Ennis (1991) found that by the end of their six-month post a small proportion claimed to have received little or no supervision, and that over half felt inadequately prepared to carry out their duties in the obstetric unit. In view of the critical medico-legal importance of supervision, such claims highlight a very serious deficiency in current practice.

However in this survey very few doctors felt supervision of patients to be frequently inadequate within their unit, although two-fifths claimed this occurred occasionally. Nevertheless, of the 11 who did say it is frequently inadequate, it was very striking that eight came from just three units (with delivery rates of 3,500–5,000). Larger units face the probability of poorer continuity of carer, and when supervision breaks down altogether, dissatisfaction rates are likely to be very high.

The midwifery survey found a much higher proportion claiming that supervision of patients is frequently inadequate. Midwives are in theory in a better position to judge whether this may be so, since they are the ones who actually give most of the one-to-one care, whereas doctors are responsible for covering perhaps several wards, including the labour ward. One post natal ward sister had claimed that 'Patients (in labour) state that they felt abandoned'. This inevitably leads to lowered satisfaction levels, and should the outcome be suboptimal, may well lead to inferences of substandard care or even negligence. While midwifery staffing levels are the concern of midwifery managers, obstetricians must be aware if the standard of care the patients receive declines because of lowered staff numbers, whether this be due to sickness or other factors. The possible legal fallout from such a situation is, sadly, easy to imagine.

Supervision of junior staff brought some notable differences of opinion: 27% of SHOs said this was frequently inadequate, compared to just 5% of consultants. One does not have to be a statistician to realize that such a discrepancy has implications for the confidence and reliability of many junior obstetricians. All of the SHOs in this survey were intending to stay in obstetrics. If these SHOs feel their supervision to be so inadequate, whether this be the responsibility of the consultant or the registrar, then their standard of work may be questioned. Legal implications, again, are all too easy to imagine.

That the relationship between junior staff and consultants is sometimes less than satisfactory was also shown by the answers to the question about how well staff felt they could rely on one another. Only one consultant out of 91 said he could always rely on junior staff to deal with potential or actual problems on the labour ward, and 27 out of 107 junior grade staff said they could always rely on their consultant in such a situation. Since the majority of legal cases originate from incidents in the labour ward or theatre areas, this does seem to be an area which ought to be addressed. Given these views it was surprising that the idea of a permanent consultant presence on the labour ward was more popular with consultants than with SHOs. Nevertheless, only half the consultants said they favoured this, despite calls for 24-hour senior cover (UK Health Departments, 1996).

It was striking to note the difference of opinion between English and Scottish hospital doctors regarding the level of responsibility accorded to midwives when looking after women deemed to be low risk: many more doctors in England said that midwives in their unit are always given full responsibility in this situation (71% compared with 29%). This large difference was echoed in the midwifery survey. It is possible to conclude that lower levels of responsibility for midwives will lead to more medical intervention, and so to lower satisfaction levels in patients. While appropriate intervention is of course desirable, there was a keenly felt sense among Scottish midwives of not being fully trusted, which can do little to improve interprofessional relationships (already noted by a significant number to be worsened by the fear of litigation).

Supervision will remain a thorny issue in today's budget-constrained health service. Reduced staffing levels must still ensure adequate standards of care. The greater flexibility required of many staff carries with it certain costs, and may contribute to stress levels and a lowering of staff morale. Managers need to assess the impact of such factors on the performance of their staff.

Fetal monitoring

CTG monitoring is another feature which has been described in the literature relating to perinatal litigation (Ennis and Vincent, 1990) and poor clinical outcomes (Scottish Office, 1994; UK Health Departments, 1996; MCHRC, 1997). There is considerable debate about its applicability (see Chapter 8), and concerns that midwives may be using it despite evidence pointing to a lack of a proven improvement in outcome (Murphy-Black, 1991). Few respondents felt this procedure to be underused, with 37% saying it is overused within their unit. A larger proportion of the Scottish doctors answered this way, mirroring the results of the midwifery survey. Claimed ability to diagnose fetal distress in an intrapartum CTG varied, with midwives rather less modest about their perceived ability than the obstetricians. Given that, in units where this procedure is used, midwives report suspected abnormalities to a doctor, this situation is anomalous.

Dover and Gauge (1995) found varying degrees of confidence in the perceived ability of midwives to interpret CTG traces, and a disturbingly low level of appropriate preparation during training. The level of training in CTG interpretation among doctors apparently varies in its effectiveness too: in this research 82% of SHOs felt this to be insufficient compared to 36% of consultants. The SHOs are usually the first doctors to be called by a midwife who suspects that an abnormality is present; for so many SHOs to feel obviously unprepared for this responsibility is clearly worrying. Also a matter of concern is the fact that 65% of the doctors felt that training of midwives in this skill is insufficient. Results from the midwifery survey showed that of those midwives based on the Labour Ward, only 14% said they had had regular updates, less than a quarter (24%) had been on a study day, 8% said their level of training had been minimal, and 5% said they had had none at all. Given the widespread use of the procedure, it is imperative that staff are well trained in its interpretation.

A related point about CTG use was under which circumstances (if any) a respondent would insist upon its use despite the clear wishes of the patient that it not be used (this question stemmed from an actual legal case). A clear difference in answer depending on grade was noted, with both junior doctors and junior midwives much more likely to say they would insist. It may be that a lack of experience will predispose to this; over reliance on the reliability and validity of CTG machines may also be more common among junior staff. However, as one obstetrician (and many midwives) pointed out, insisting on a procedure such as this carries potential dangers, one of which is a possible charge of trespass or even assault. Even if this does not arise, the dissatisfaction engendered may well predispose to complaints being brought against staff. While these are unlikely on their own to initiate legal proceedings, insensitive handling of such complaints has been known to promote further disputes between patients and staff.

Workplace relationships

Failures in 'cross-discipline collaboration' and communication have been highlighted as factors in, respectively, maternal deaths (UK Health Departments, 1996) and stillbirths and deaths in infancy (MCHRC, 1997). It seems self-evident that workplace relationships must be good if the delivery of health care is not to suffer, but this is apparently not always the case: Kitzinger et al (1990) describe relations between doctors and midwives as 'highly charged and traditionally antagonistic'.

The claim made by the former Chief Medical Officer, Sir Donald Acheson, about interprofessional relationships in the delivery room being poisoned by the fear of litigation produced a mixed response. Junior grade doctors, who probably spend more time in the delivery room than most of their consultant colleagues, were more likely to agree. On the whole slightly more midwives than doctors agreed with the view as well, and again it was the more junior midwives (who work most often in direct contact with patients and junior doctors) who were most likely to agree. If these feelings are as widespread as they appear amongst junior clinical staff, then again a teaching programme which educates clinicians about the law as it affects clinical practice would seem to be essential. Deteriorating doctor-midwife relationships in an area as critical as the delivery room is surely a recipe for disaster, with practitioners developing a tendency to point the finger of blame whenever outcomes are less than optimal. Scottish hospital doctors were more likely to agree or strongly agree than their English counterparts (36% compared with 24%). In the midwifery matched pairs trial, the Scottish midwives were much more likely to agree strongly, although when 'Agree' and 'Strongly agree' were merged this distinction disappeared.

While, broadly speaking, attitudes towards communication and rapport between doctors and midwives showed similar overall responses from the two professions, many midwives were far less generous about the nature of their relationships with doctors than the doctors were about their relationships with midwives. Over half the midwives described these as 'Fair' at best when things were deemed to have gone wrong (almost 15% described them as 'Poor' or 'Terrible'), which does not indicate harmony in the workplace.

An improvement in communication between service providers and users, as noted in Chapter 9, has been a target for many involved in maternity care. The amount of information available to pregnant women and new mothers, in the form of booklets and leaflets, appears to have grown exponentially in recent years, but despite this there is still doubt about how much information actually gets across. The Changing Childbirth report noted that 'all too often it is left to the patient to ask about a service' (DoH, 1993b), and even then it appears that many health professionals are not in a position to provide answers (*ibid*).

Communication and rapport between practitioners and patients were generally felt by doctors in this survey to be good; even when things go wrong doctors appear to feel that relations do not deteriorate to an unacceptable level. Midwives once again were more pessimistic in their outlook. If such relationships are poor at a time when empathetic communication and sympathy are essential, then the incidence of complaints and legal claims may be expected to rise. Many midwives pointed out in their survey that the government has given the right (some would say the encouragement) to complain to patients, and undoubtedly many are taking advantage of the procedures which are publicized in the Patients' Charter and other similar local publications.

Some of those midwives who had experienced litigation had harrowing tales to tell. Many seemed to feel isolated from colleagues, and there were strongly voiced opinions that managers were not supportive. The antagonisms which arise in such situations can be addressed at least in part by tactful dealings with staff, and sensitive claims management. Some areas have instigated perinatal outcomes analysis, which aims to clarify the issues involved in such situations by identifying the relevant staff and getting them to document clearly their involvement in the events which have led to a poor outcome. Not only does this (hopefully) shed light on the events in question, but, if done sensitively, will allow the staff concerned to focus on their practice and perhaps admit to deficiencies. A sure way to get staff to 'clam up' is to make such procedures a mechanism for apportioning blame. The focus must be on constructive evaluation, but until such developments become widespread, there will always be the possibility that staff will become isolated when complaints come in, particularly when the complaint is in the form of a formal legal action, as frequently happens.

Choice

The concept of choice for pregnant women in maternity care is problematic, particularly when dealing with the notions of professionalism and – some would say – paternalism. The Changing Childbirth report noted with reference to one area that improvements were needed because 'women were not aware of choices available to them in childbirth' (DoH, 1993b). Following research into interventions in labour in England and Wales, Renfrew (1989), asks if 'women only have choice when we approve of that choice?' As if answering this the Winterton report noted that 'although they lent their support to the principle of providing "the maximum choice to the mother", the RCOG added the rider "consistent with the best possible level of care"' (House of Commons, 1992).

Midwives have also been criticized for failing to provide real choice: 'Although lip service is paid to the concepts of informed consent and continuity of care, I believe all that has really improved is the social skill required to persuade women to accept those interventions which make the system easier to administer ...' (Hobbs, 1997). This view may appear rather jaundiced, but there is no doubt that many midwives feel torn between the desire to ensure minimal intervention in a labour, and the fear that by doing so they may be missing evidence of fetal compromise. In part this reflects the midwife's own degree of confidence, but as Dimond (1993) points out, midwives may be losing confidence because their own role as a provider of normal midwifery care has been eroded over the years. This lack of confidence in their own skills means that in turn they are not in a position to give women real choice.

Whether care is prescribed on a genuinely individual basis or through the implementation of protocols and policies largely determines how much real choice is available. Churchill (1995) believes that 'women are asked to consent to interventionist techniques (but) may do so without really understanding what the procedures entail. In such cases it is questionable whether the consent given by the woman represents free choice'.

The notions of choice and control are linked with the debate about midwifery professional autonomy. It can be argued that in wresting a measure of control from doctors midwives are playing the same patriarchal games which obstetricians have played for years (Oakley, 1984; Witz, 1992). Ralston (1994) notes that 'the whole issue of choice for women is really about power and control'. Elsewhere I discuss the moves towards midwifery professionalization and the tension between displaying professional characteristics (such as control) and devolving real decision-making to the pregnant woman (Symon, 1996). Bluff and Holloway (1994) found in their research that 'the women trusted the midwives because of their expertise. No matter what happened during the labour process and the birth of the baby, the trust remained intact ... the core construct proved to be the belief that "they know best".'

There is of course a fine balance to be struck between providing the level of choice demanded by government reports (House of Commons, 1992; DoH, 1993a; Scottish

Office, 1993) and exerting a certain degree of control in the desire to ensure a good clinical outcome.

Nevertheless, it does seem clear that routine treatments or procedures are the norm in maternity care, and that even when a woman specifically refuses certain procedures they may still be carried out. The fear that the woman's decisions may not be adequately informed, and that she may in consequence contribute to a poor outcome, is evident from the fact that almost two-thirds of respondents said they would monitor a woman in labour using electronic equipment even when she had specifically refused this. Such a dilemma cannot be easily resolved; continuing education, both of midwives and the women under their care, will help to reduce such instances occurring, but it would be naive to think that resolution will be speedy or without acrimony.

Complaints and counselling

The level of complaints has apparently been increasing sharply. Complaining is one way whereby patients can call practitioners to account, yet it was evident that some respondents believe that complaints by patients are taken at face value, regardless of their merits. However, the Winterton report found that many women apparently encounter difficulties in making a complaint, describing the process as 'too complicated, stressful and often fruitless' (House of Commons, 1992), and concluding that 'the complaints system is failing to achieve the purpose for which it was designed, at least so far as the maternity services are concerned. This failure may be causing earlier and more frequent recourse to litigation ...' (*ibid*).

From this survey the actual incidence of complaints appears fairly high (these complaints all related to staff attitudes). Forty-one per cent of the doctors said they had been the subject of such a complaint, a far greater proportion than the 17% of midwives who admitted that they had been the subject of one. While it is unclear what the relationship is (if any) between initial complaint and subsequent legal action (although this has shown this to happen on occasion (Symon, 1998), dissatisfied patients do appear more ready to have recourse to legal action than was once the case. It would be foolish to dismiss the apparent rising tide of complaints as being no more than a fashion induced by the Patients' Charter. Claims management aims to ensure that complaints are dealt with in such a way as to deflect frivolous claims while acknowledging the nature of genuine complaints, and offering apology and, where necessary (and after due legal advice), compensation. The theory of claims management notwithstanding, Robinson (1997) depicts a rather jaundiced view of the practice and effectiveness of giving explanations.

The procedure by which complaints concerning hospital staff are made changed in April 1996. There is now a requirement that complaints are made within six months (or up to 12 months if a good reason can be given). While this will almost certainly simplify the process of investigation, it has been criticized by one consumer organisation, who point out that some women may take much longer to become emotionally prepared for the process of complaining formally (Robinson, 1996).

The quality of counselling is critical, and must be taken into account (UK Health Departments, 1996). From this survey the presence at least of formal review/counselling procedures for patients who have had an adverse outcome to their pregnancy or labour appears to be fairly widespread: 63% of the doctors claimed that such exist within their unit. In three (all GP units) of the 31 units surveyed, no such procedures were claimed to exist. However, as already mentioned, doctors from the same unit were often not of the same opinion regarding the existence of counselling.

Given the importance being attached to risk management strategies, a similar investment in claims management would seem in order. This could effect a large reduction in the number of actively pursued complaints and claims which come in and which are the result of dissatisfaction or disappointment at a less than optimal outcome rather than a genuine belief that negligence has occurred. Such claims must still be investigated, and if the initial complaint is not made for months or even years (as is commonplace) the complicated process of enquiry can take a long time, inducing much stress and anxiety among the staff concerned. Formal review procedures available soon after the event ought, in theory, to head off those claims which are made on the basis of a misunderstanding, and ought to preempt the tortuous retrospective enquiry process which is so often required at present. Counselling cannot be assumed to be effective: one midwife stated that the standard of such procedures in her unit were 'very poor'. Continuous review of counselling procedures, together with suitable training for the staff involved, are essential.

Community staff

This research was heavily slanted towards perinatal care which is hospital-based, since legal cases have tended to concern events or allegations which centre on the care given by a midwife or obstetrician while working in hospital. This meant that some parts of the survey were not of direct relevance to all the midwives, although with moves towards integrating community-based and hospital-based midwives, such distinctions may be of less relevance in the future. Nevertheless many community-based respondents added comments about the relationship they hold with GPs and it is clear that tension is present in many areas, a tension which diminishes the effectiveness of health care. Calls for Community midwives to have more intrapartum experience were common, and this is one area which could certainly be addressed in order to help give more genuine choice to pregnant women, particularly in rural areas. How these midwives tackle the unwillingness on the part of some GPs to accept their role in promoting such choice is less clear, but it seems obvious that little will improve without open and honest communication between all parties. Many community-based respondents appeared to feel that a large number of GPs either misunderstand the role of the midwife, or mistrust her skills and abilities.

The answers of GPs in this survey were often different to those of the hospital based doctors. All the GPs were from areas at some distance from the urban centres of Scotland; some were from the islands. This geographical remove is apparently reflected to a degree in their perceptions of this subject: between them they conduct or are responsible for few deliveries compared with the hospital based doctors. The prevalence of litigation is likely to be minimal in such circumstances. Given the fact that none of the women booked under a GP scheme will be predicted to be at high risk, the rate of suboptimal outcome ought to be very much lower than in hospital, and the consequent dissatisfaction rate negligible. It has been claimed that, with the continuity of care which GPs enjoy, particularly in the more remote rural areas, the likelihood of dissatisfaction among patients is significantly reduced.

GPs were less likely to believe litigation has increased, and in fact only two (out of 21) had ever been involved in a legal action. None had considered abandoning obstetrics because of litigation. They were as likely as the Scottish hospital doctors, however, to say they had changed their practice as a result of the fear of litigation: almost always this entailed quicker referrals to a consultant unit when problems arise or are suspected. This is perceived by many community midwives as a lack of confidence on the part of GPs, and strong tensions in the GP-midwife relationship were evident from responses in the midwifery survey.

GPs were in fact the most likely of the groups to believe that financial pressures within the health service may make clinical practice less safe, although what changes they envisaged is not known. Some GPs clearly felt that they could do with more training to deal with obstetric emergencies, transfer to consultant unit from remote areas, particularly in winter, being problematic. Deficiencies in neonatal resuscitation were highlighted by the Confidential Enquiry into Stillbirths and Deaths in Infancy; training for GPs and Community Midwives is essential if the choice of delivering in a small rural unit or at home is to be offered to pregnant women. However, given the overall low number of such deliveries, and the fact that predicted high risk patients will in theory already be transferred to a consultant unit, the time and money for such training in community-based staff may not easily be found.

Neonatal staff

Within the hospital setting cases have largely turned on events in the labour period, and the questionnaire reflected this. There are a number of perinatal cases which involve the neonatal period, however, and so I was keen to obtain information about the attitudes of midwives working in such units. Fewer additional comments on this subject were offered; within some neonatal units 'midwife status' has apparently been rescinded, practitioners now being employed as neonatal nurses. It may be that such moves are lessening some individuals' concept of themselves as a midwife, although it is clear that many who work long term in such units maintain their RCM membership rather than join another professional body.

In some legal cases concerning cerebral palsy the distinction between 'obstetrics' and 'neonatal paediatrics' is very fine from the point of view of causation. Acheson (1991) points out that cerebral palsy can be caused at any time in the development of the brain, which can be 'as early as the first three months of pregnancy or as late as early infancy'. The majority of legal cases have centred on the labour period, but there are cases which have alleged negligence on the part of neonatal staff.

One neonatal midwife commented that she'd seen a number of babies damaged by asphyxial insults during labour which had been preventable. This may be true, but there is a danger that the view can be taken that it is only intrapartum insults which affect the baby, and that such intrapartum insults are always avoidable. As indicated earlier in this report, there is a need for midwives to educate the public that this is not so, and that in some cases where asphyxia is present during labour the asphyxia is a symptom of an underlying problem, and not the result of poor care.

Some legal cases have become complicated because neonatal staff (medical or midwifery) have suggested to parents that their baby's poor condition at or soon after birth is due to events in labour (Symon, 1997d). While this may be the case, such assertions should never be made before a full investigation has been carried out to determine whether or not this is so. The damage to staff-patient relationships by unwarranted claims of this nature may be immense.

Conclusion

This research has allowed the views of practitioners concerning litigation to be heard, and it is hoped that these views will allow the debate about litigation to move forward. While not attempting to be the last word on the subject, the large scale of the survey allows for fairly firm conclusions to be drawn about these views. Although the surveys largely comprised respondents based in Scotland, and some interesting cross-Border differences of opinion were noted, there were also many areas in which perceptions in Scotland and England were very similar. The results, then, are relevant in both countries. Most practitioners believe litigation has increased, and view it as a distinct threat, despite little publicly-available data which might confirm their suspicions or fears. Interestingly, most of those with a direct experience of litigation did not seem to be unduly affected, although of course reactions varied.

While a number of assertions about staff reactions have been aired in the literature, many of these claims did not appear to be based on sound research. Anecdotal evidence may reflect reality, but its veracity can only truly be tested through surveying a large sample. The surveys have done this, and while they have confirmed litigation as a significant feature of modern clinical practice, its effects ought not to be over-stated. While most respondents believed practice generally to be becoming defensive, a smaller proportion admitted that they had personally changed practice, and there was little evidence of a potential haemorrhage of practitioners. However, many staff are clearly worried about possible litigation; its effects may be significant in individual cases, and managers have a duty to ensure that those staff who are involved receive appropriate support.

Several respondents mentioned their concern at the apparent lack of protection of the rights of the unborn child when attempting to allow the woman autonomy and decision making. The tension between wanting to allow women to exercise choice, and the desire to protect oneself from the accusation that care has been substandard (for instance because monitoring was not carried out and a baby has been born with a degree of handicap) is a very real one for midwives, particularly those working at the 'sharp end' of care, the labour period.

Many features related to litigation have been confirmed as being of critical importance. Autonomy and choice for the pregnant woman at times sit uneasily with the perceptions many practitioners have of what is required of them. Trying to ensure that their standard of care is satisfactory, and trying to prevent or pre-empt any allegation of negligence, leads some practitioners to assert control over the pregnant or labouring woman. This runs counter to the spirit of modern maternity care, but appears at times to be inevitable in a working environment which seems very conscious of the possibility of litigation.

A solution (easy to prescribe and yet difficult to implement) is to improve communication and understanding between different professional groups, and between users and providers of maternity services. While it may seem trite and obvious to advocate better communication, there is no doubt that failures in this art are significant contributors both to the incidence of suboptimal outcomes and to the distrustful and adversarial atmosphere which results, and which can do so much to foment litigation.

Practitioners must be accountable; the question of blame is very much more complex, and focusing on blame does little to promote confident practice, or confidence among those women who seek maternity care.

Glossary

AIMS	Association for Improvements in the Maternity Services
Apgar score	Method of assessing condition of newborn baby
Auscultation	Listening to the fetal heart sounds (rate and rhythm)
CPAP	Continuous Positive Airways Pressure
CTG	Cardiotocography (see also EFM)
Chorion villus sampling	Early pregnancy diagnostic test
DGH	District General Hospital
EFM	Electronic Fetal Monitoring (see also CTG)
FHR	Fetal Heart Rate
MRU	Midwife Run Unit
'paed'	Paediatrician
PET	Pre-eclamptic toxaemia
PIH	Pregnancy Induced Hypertension
Pinard(s)	Stethoscope for listening to fetal heart rate
SANDS	Stillbirth And Neonatal Death Society
Sonicaid	Electronic device for listening to fetal heart rate
Syntocinon	Drug given to stimulate (augment) labour
Syntometrine	Drug given to help separation of placenta
TAMBA	Twins And Multiple Birth Association
Venflon	Cannula used to give intravenous drugs and fluids
Ventouse	Method of instrumental delivery using suction

References

Acheson, D. (1991). 'Are obstetrics and midwifery doomed?' *Midwives' Chronicle*, Vol. 104 (1,241): 158–66.

Anon (1990). 'Medical Negligence: Hunter v Hanley 35 years on.' *Scots Law Times*, p. 325.

Anon (1997a). 'Former midwives' leader pays £0.8m damages for baby with cerebral palsy'. *Nursing Standard*, Vol. 11, No. 22: 8.

Anon (1997b). 'Bereaved family face legal fight'. *The Herald*, 31.5.97: 9.

Apgar, V. (1953). 'Proposal for a new method of evaluation of newborn infants'. *Anaesthesia and Analgesia*, Vol. 32: 260–67.

Atiyah, P., Cane, P. (1993). *Accidents, Compensation and the Law* (5th edition). London: Weidenfield and Nicolson.

Audit Commission (1997). *First Class Delivery: Improving Maternity Services in England and Wales.* Audit Commission for Local Authorities and the NHS in England and Wales.

Baldwin, L-M., Larson, E., Hart, L., Greer, T., Lloyd, M., Rosenblatt, R. (1991). 'Characteristics of physicians with obstetric malpractice claims experience'. *Obstetrics and Gynecology*, Vol. 78 (6): 1050–54.

Bastian, H. (1990). 'Obstetrics and litigation: a consumer perspective'. *Medical Journal of Australia*, Vol. 153: 340–45.

Beazley, J. (1995). 'Natural labour and its active management.' In:Whitfield C. R., (Ed) *Dewhurst's Textbook of Obstetrics and Gynaecology for Postgraduates*. Oxford: Blackwell Scientific.

Beech, B. (1984). *'Perinatal Services and Prenatal Care – User Perspective'*. WHO – appropriate technology for birth. AIMS publications.

Beech, B. (1986). *'Childbirth in Hospital: the Choice of the Mother or the Right of the Child.'* (London Medical Group Symposium). AIMS publications.

Beech, B. (1989). 'Commentary'. In: Francome, C. (Ed). *Changing Childbirth*. London: Maternity Alliance.

Beech, B. (1990). 'Accountability and compensation'. *AIMS Quarterly Journal*, Vol. 2 (4): 1–3.

Beech, B. (1992). *Penalties of Obstetric Technology.* (2nd International Homebirth Conference). AIMS publications.

Begley, C. (1986). 'Episiotomy – use or abuse?' *Nursing Review*, Vol. 4: 4–7.

Black, N. (1990). 'Medical litigation and the quality of care'. *Lancet*,Vol. 335: 35–37.

Blackie, J. (1985). 'Scotland'. In: Deutsch, Schriber (Eds). *Medical Responsibility in Western Europe* Berlin, New York: Springer-Verlag.

Blair, E. (1993). 'A research definition for 'Birth Asphyxia'?' *Developmental Medicine and Child Neurology*, Vol. 35: 449–55.

Blair, E., Stanley, F. (1988). 'Intrapartum asphyxia: a rare cause of cerebral palsy'. *Journal of Pediatrics [Australia]*, Vol. 112: 515–19.

Bluff, R., Holloway, I. (1994). 'They know best: women's perceptions of midwifery care during labour and childbirth.' *Midwifery*, Vol. 10, No. 3: 157–64.

Blunt, S. (1991). 'Training in obstetrics.' *British Medical Journal*, Vol. 303: 1416.

BMA (1987). *No Fault Compensation Working Party Report*. London: British Medical Association.

Bowles, R., Jones, P. (1989). 'A health authority's experience'. *New Law Journal*, Vol. 139:119–23.

Brahams, D. (1991). 'Worried obstetricians'. *Lancet*, Vol. 337: 1597.

Brahams, M. (1988). '"No Fault" in Finland: paying patients and drug victims'. *New Law Journal*, Sept 23: 678–81.

Brazier, M. (1987). *Medicine, Patients, and the Law*. Harmondsworth: Penguin.

Brocklehurst, P., Duley, L., MacFarlane, A., Garcia, J., Elbourne, D. (1995). 'Conclusions are not supported by results'. (letter) *British Medical Journal*, Vol. 310: 806.

Brown, P. (1990). 'How to state your case'. *Nursing Times* Vol. 86: No. 38: 52.

Brown, W. (1985). *The Law and the Nurse in Scotland*. Newcastle upon Tyne Polytechnic Products.

Campbell, R., MacFarlane, A. (1986). 'Place of delivery: a review'. *British Journal of Obstetrics and Gynaecology*, Vol. 93: 675–83.

Capstick, J., Edwards, P. (1990). 'Trends in obstetric malpractice claims'. *Lancet*, Vol. 336: 931–32

Carson, D. (1988). 'Medical accident litigation'. *The Health Service Journal*, January 21.

Cetrulo, C., Cetrulo, L. (1989). 'The legal liability of the medical consultant in pregnancy.' *Medical Clinics of North America*, Vol. 73 (3): 557–65.

Chamberlain, G. (1992). *How to Avoid Medico-legal Problems in Obstetrics and Gynaecology*. London: RCOG.

Chamberlain, G. (1995). *Obstetrics by Ten Teachers* (16th edition). London, Boston, Sydney, Auckland: Arnold.

Charles, J., Curtis, L. (1994). 'Birth afterthoughts: a listening and information service.' *British Journal of Midwifery*, Vol. 2 (7): 331–34.

Churchill, H. (1995). 'Perceptions of childbirth: are women properly informed?' *Nursing Times*, Vol. 91, No. 45: 32–33.

Clements, R. (1991). 'Litigation in obstetrics and gynaecology'. *British Journal of Obstetrics and Gynaecology*, Vol. 98: 423–26.

Crowther, M. (1995). 'Communication following stillbirth or neonatal death: room for improvement.' *British Journal of Obstetrics and Gynaecology*, Vol. 102: 952–56.

Dimond, B. (1993). 'Client autonomy and choice'. *Modern Midwife*, 2/93: 15–16.

Dimond, B. (1994). *The Legal Aspects of Midwifery*. Hale: Books for Midwives Press.

Dingwall, R. (1986). 'Maternity care at a premium?' *Nursing Times* Vol. 82; May 7; 38–39.

Dingwall, R. (1991). 'Risk management'. *British Medical Journal*, Vol. 302: 255.

Dingwall, R., Fenn, P. (1991). 'Is risk management necessary?' *International Journal of Risk and Safety in Medicine*, Vol. 2: 91–106.

Dingwall, R., Fenn, P., Quam, L. (1991). *Medical Negligence – A Review and Bibliography*. Oxford: Centre for Socio-Legal Studies.

DoH [Department of Health] (1991). *Arbitration for Medical Negligence in the National Health Service*. London: HMSO.

DoH [Department of Health] (1993a). *Changing Childbirth. Report of Expert Maternity Group* (the Cumberlege report). London: HMSO.

DoH [Department of Health] (1993b). *Changing Childbirth – Part II: Survey of Good Communications Practice in Maternity Services*. London: HMSO.

DoH [Department of Health] (1996). *Guidance on Implementation of the NHS Complaints Procedure*. London: HMSO.

Doherty, R., James, C. (1994). 'Malpractice in obstetrics and gynaecology'. In: Bonnar, J. (Ed) *Recent Advances in Obstetrics and Gynaecology* Vol. 17: 91–106.

Dornan, J. (1990). 'Avoiding medico-legal problems in labour'. In: *Contemporary Reviews in Obstetrics and Gynaecology*, Vol. 2, No. 3: 159–62.

Dover, S., Gauge S. (1995). 'Fetal monitoring – midwifery attitudes.' *Midwifery*, Vol. 11, No. 1: 18–27.

Durward, L., Evans, R. (1990). 'Pressure groups and maternity care'. In: Garcia, J., Kilpatrick, R., Richards, M. (Eds) *The Politics of Maternity Care*. Oxford: Clarendon Paperbacks. pp. 256–73.

Dyer, C. (1990). 'Pressure for no fault on three fronts'. *British Medical Journal*, Vol. 301: 1010.

Easterbrook, J. (1996). 'Medical negligence update.' *Solicitors' Journal*, Vol. 140: 381.

Edwards, D., Mason P. (1993). *Litigation – A Risk Management Guide for Midwives*. RCM: Capsticks.

Edwards, N. (1996) 'Is everything rosy in the MSLC garden?' *AIMS Journal*, Vol. 8, No.3: 6–9.

Ennis, M. (1991). 'Training and supervision of obstetric senior house officers.' *British Medical Journal*, Vol. 303: 1442–43.

Ennis, M., Vincent, C. A. (1990), 'Obstetric accidents: a review of 64 cases.' *British Medical Journal*, Vol. 300: 1365–67.

Ennis, M., Clark, A., Grudzinskas, J. G. (1991) 'Change in obstetric practice in response to fear of litigation in the British isles.' *Lancet*, 338: 616.

Etzioni, A. (1975) 'Alternative conceptions of accountability.' In: Greenfield, H. (Ed). *Accountability in Health Facilities* New York: Praeger Publishers.

Fenn, P., Dingwall, R. (1989). 'Medical negligence and crown indemnity'. In: *Health Care UK 1989*. Hermitage Berks Policy Journals.

Fenn, P., Dingwall, R. (1995). 'Mutual trust?' *British Medical Journal*, Vol. 310: 756.

Fisher, C. (1990). 'No-fault insurance in obstetrics.' *Medical Journal of Australia* 153: 639–41.

Flamm, B. (1990). 'Was the death of this baby avoidable?' *Birth* Vol. 17, No. 4: 226–27.

Francome, C. (1986). 'The fashion for caesareans'. *New Society*, 17.1.86: 100.

Gaffney, G., Sellers, S., Flavell, V., Squier, M., Johnson, A. (1994). 'Case-control study of intrapartum care, cerebral palsy, and perinatal death'. *British Medical Journal*, Vol. 308: 743–50.

Garcia, J., Garforth, S., Ayers, S. (1985). 'Midwives confined? Labour ward policies and routines'. In: Thomson, A., Robinson, S (Eds). *Research and the Midwife* [conference proceedings] Nursing Research Unit, University of London.

Genn, H., Lloyd-Bostock, S. (1990). 'Medical negligence – major new research in progress'. *Journal of the Medical Defence Union*, Vol. 6: 42–43.

GMC [General Medical Council] (1989). *Professional Conduct and Discipline: Fitness to Practice*. London: GMC.

Goldrein, I. (1994). 'Exploding the Bolam myth'. *New Law Journal*, Sept. 16–Oct 28 1994 (seven weekly articles, pp. 1237–481).

Grant, A., Joy, M-T., O'Brien, N., Hennessy, E., MacDonald, D. (1989). 'Cerebral palsy among children born during the Dublin randomised trial of intrapartum monitoring'. *Lancet*, Vol. 334: 1233–36.

Greenfield, H. (1975) *Accountability in Health Facilities*. New York: Praeger Publishers.

Hall, C. (1991) 'Obstetric legal settlements centre on instruments'. *The Independent*, 3.6.91.

Ham, C., Dingwall, R., Fenn, P., Harris, D. (1988). *'Medical Negligence: Compensation and Accountability'*. London: King's Fund Institute.

Haverkamp, A., Thompson, H., McFee, J., Cetrulo, C. (1976). 'The evaluation of continuous FHR monitoring in high risk pregnancy'. *American Journal of Obstetrics and Gynecology*, Vol. 125: 310–20.

Hawkins, C., Paterson, I. (1987). 'Medico-legal audit in the West Midlands region: analysis of 100 cases'. *British Medical Journal*, Vol. 295: 1533–36.

Henderson, A. (1993). 'Midwifery-led care'. *Nursing Times* (27.1.93) 89:4:18.

Hensleigh, P., Fainstat, T., Spencer, R. (1986). 'Perinatal events and cerebral palsy'. *American Journal of Obstetrics and Gynecology*, Vol. 154 (5): 978–81.

Hobbs, L. (1997). 'Is that clearly understood?' *Modern Midwife*, Vol. 7, No. 1: 18–19.

Hough, M., Mayhew, P. (1985). *'The British Crime Survey, (First Report)'*. London: HMSO.

House of Commons (1992). Health Committee: *Volume 1 of the Second Report on the Maternity Services* (Chairman: Winterton, N.). London: HMSO.

Howie, R. (1983). 'The standard of care in medical negligence'. *Juridical Review*, 193.

Hughes, D., Goldstone, L. (1989). 'Midwifery monitor II: Labour care'. Poly Enterprises (Leeds) Ltd.

Hundley, V., Cruikshank, F., Lang, G., Glazener, C., Milne, J., Turner, M., Blyth, D., Mollison, J., Donaldson, C. (1994). 'Midwife managed delivery unit: a randomised controlled comparison with consultant led care'. *British Medical Journal*, Vol. 309: 1400–404.

ISD [Information and Statistics Division of the National Health Service in Scotland] (1996) *Scottish Stillbirth and Infant Death Report 1995*. Edinburgh: HMSO.

James, C. (1991). 'Risk management in obstetrics and gynaecology'. *Journal of the Medical Defence Union*, Vol. 7, No.2: 3363–38.

James, D. (1995). 'Obstetricians should focus on problems.' *British Medical Journal*, Vol. 310: 37–38.

Jones, I. (1995). 'Study shows interventionist nature of British obstetrics'. (letter) *British Medical Journal*, Vol. 301: 806.

Jones, O., Smith, S. (1996). 'Choosing the place of birth.' *British Journal of Midwifery*, Vol. 4: 140.

Kitzinger, J., Green, J., Coupland, V. (1990). 'Labour relations: midwives and doctors on the Labour Ward'. In: Garcia, J., Kilpatrick, R., Richards, M. (Eds). *The Politics of Maternity Care* Oxford: Clarendon Paperbacks. pp 149–62.

Kitzinger, S., Walters, R. (1981). 'Some women's experience of episiotomy'. London: National Childbirth Trust.

Klein, R. (1973). *Complaints Against Doctors*. London: C. Knight.

Lamont, L. (1993). 'Why patients don't sue doctors'. *Journal of the Medical Defence Union*, Vol. 9, No. 2: 39–41.

Levene, M., Sands, C., Grindulis, H., Moore, J. (1986). 'Comparison of two methods of predicting outcome in perinatal asphyxia'. *Lancet*, Vol. 327: 67–68.

Little, W. (1861). 'On the influence of abnormal parturition, difficult labours, premature births, and asphyxia neonatorum on the mental and physical condition of the child especially in relation to deformities'. *Transactions of the Obstetrical Society of London*.

Logue, M. (1991). 'Putting research into practice: perineal management during delivery'. In: Robinson, S., Thomson, A. (Eds). *Midwives, Research and Childbirth*, Volume 2 London: Chapman and Hall.

Luthy, D., Shy, K., van belle, G., Larson, E., Hughes, J., Benedetti, T., Brown, Z. (1987). 'A randomised trial of electronic fetal monitoring in preterm labor'. *Obstetrics and Gynecology*, Vol. 69: 687–95.

Lyall, J. (1988) 'High costs of failure'. *Health Service Journal*, 24.3.88: 334.

MacDonald, D., Grant, A., Sheridan-Pereira, M., Boylan, P., Chalmers, I. (1985). 'The Dublin randomised controlled trial of intrapartum fetal heart rate monitoring'. *American Journal of Obstetrics and Gynecology*, Vol. 152: 524–39.

MacFarlane, A., Mugford, M. (1984). *Birth Counts*. London: HMSO.

Mander, R. (1993). 'Who chooses the choices?' *Modern Midwife*, 2/93: 23–25.

Mansell, W. (1997). 'Tort and socio-legal studies. The road to Damascus: paved with good intentions but few Epiphanies'. In: Thomas, P. (Ed.) *Socio-Legal Studies*: Aldershot, Dartmouth. pp 222–38.

Marlow, N. (1992). 'Do we need an Apgar score?' *Archives of Disease in Childhood*, Vol. 67: 765–69.

MCHRC [Maternal and Child Health Research Consortium] (1997). *Confidential Enquiry into Stillbirths and Deaths in Infancy*. London: MCHRC.

McLean, S. (1988). 'No fault liability and medical responsibility'. In: Freeman, M (Ed). *Medicine, Ethics and the Law* London: Stevens and Sons.

MPS [Medical Protection Society] (1989). *Annual Report*. London: Medical Protection Society.

Murphy, K., Johnson, P., Moorcraft, J., Pattinson, J., Russell, V., Turnbull, A. (1990). 'Birth asphyxia and the intrapartum cardiotocograph'. *British Journal of Obstetrics and Gynaecology*, Vol. 97: 470–79.

Murphy-Black, T. (1991). 'Fetal monitoring in labour.' *Nursing Times*, Vol. 87, No. 28: 58–59.

Nelson, K., Ellenberg, J. (1981). 'Apgar scores as predictors of chronic neurologic disability'. *Pediatrics*, Vol. 68: 36–44.

Nielsen, P., Stigsby, B., Nickelsen, C., Nim, J. (1987). 'Intra- and inter-observer variability in the assessment of intrapartum CTGs'. *Acta Obstetrica et Gynecologica Scandinavica*, Vol. 66: 421–24.

Norrie, K. (1985). 'Medical negligence: who sets the standard?' *Journal of Medical Ethics*, Vol. 11: 135–37.

Oakley, A. (1984). *The Captured Womb*. Oxford: Blackwell.

Oliphant, K. (1996). 'Defining "Medical misadventure". Lessons from New Zealand'. *Medical Law Review*, Vol. 4: 1–31.

Pearson, Lord (Chairman) (1978). *Royal Commission on Civil Liability and Compensation for Personal Injury*. Cmnd 7054. London: HMSO.

Pinker, G. (1991). 'Accountability: is there a better system?' In: *Compensation and Accountability – Keeping the Balance*. Proceedings of MDU conference.

Powers, J., Harris, N. (Eds). (1995). *Medical Negligence*. London: Butterworths.

Ralston, R. (1994). 'How much choice do women really have in relation to their care?' *British Journal of Midwifery*, Vol. 2, No. 9: 453–56.

Ranjan, V. (1993). 'Obstetrics and the fear of litigation'. *Professional Care of Mother and Child*, January 1993; 10–12.

Reid, N., Reid, R., Morris, D. (1995). 'Customer complaints in the National Health Service.' *Journal of Nursing Management*, Vol. 3: 295–99.

Renfrew, M. (1989). Commentary. In: Francome, C. (Ed). *Changing Childbirth* London: Maternity Alliance.

Roberts, G. (1993). 'If only a caesarean had been carried out.' *Journal of the Medical Defence Union*, Vol. 9: 76–78.

Robinson, J. (1996). 'The new complaints system: snakes and ladders.' *AIMS Journal*, Vol. 8, No.2: 9–11.

Robinson, J. (1997). 'How to get sued: the step by step guide to increase litigation against your trust.' *British Journal of Midwifery*, Vol. 5: 641.

Rosenberger, L. (1995). 'Charting fundamentals'. *Midwifery Today*, Vol. 33: 23–25.

Ruth, V., Raivio, K. (1988). 'Perinatal brain damage: predictive value of metabolic acidosis and the Apgar score'. *British Medical Journal*, Vol. 297: 24–27.

Saunders, P. (1992). 'Recruitment in obstetrics and gynaecology: RCOG sets initiatives'. *British Journal of Obstetrics and Gynaecology* Vol. 99: 538–40.

Scottish Office (1993). *The Provision of Maternity Services in Scotland: A Policy Review*. Edinburgh: Scottish Office Home and Health Department.

Scottish Office (1994). *Report on Maternal and Perinatal Deaths in Scotland 1986–1990*. Edinburgh: HMSO.

Sharp, D., Chamberlain, G. (1992). 'Doctors' concerns about litigation'. In: Chamberlain, G (Ed). *How to Avoid Medico-legal Problems in Obstetrics and Gynaecology* London: RCOG.

Shy, K., Luthy, D., Bennett, F., Whitfield, M., Larson, E., van Belle, G., Hughes, J. (1990). 'Effects of electronic fetal heart rate monitoring as compared with periodic auscultation on the neurologic development of premature infants'. *New England Journal of Medicine*, Vol. 332: 588–93.

Sikorski, J., Wilson. J., Clement, S., Das, S., Smeeton, N. (1996). 'A randomised controlled trial comparing two schedules of antenatal visits: the antenatal care project'. *British Medical Journal*, Vol. 312: 546–53.

Simanowitz, A. (1987). 'Medical accidents: the problem and the challenge'. In: Byrne P (Ed). *Medicine in Contemporary Society*. London: King Edwards Hospital Fund for London.

Simanowitz, A. (1989). Commentary. In: Francome, C. (Ed). *Changing Childbirth*. London: Maternity Alliance.

Simmons, S. (1990). 'Compensation for damage at birth' (letter). *The Times*, 13.12.90.

Sleep, J. (1984). 'West Berkshire perineal management trial'. *British Medical Journal*, Vol. 289: 587–90.

Smith, J., Mitchell, S. (1996). 'Debriefing after childbirth: a tool for effective risk management'. *British Journal of Midwifery*, Vol. 4, No. 11: 581–86.

Smith, L. (1995). 'Analysis is invalid'. (letter) *British Medical Journal*, Vol. 301: 805–806.

Smith, R. (1988). 'No stopping no fault'. *British Medical Journal*, Vol. 297: 935–36.

Somerset, D., O'Donnell, E. (1995). 'Care in a midwife managed delivery unit may not be the best option' (letter). *British Medical Journal*, Vol. 301: 805.

Stapleton, J. (1994). 'In restraint of tort'. In: Birks, P. (Ed). *The Frontiers of Liability* Vol. 2. Oxford: OUP.

Symon, A. (1996). 'Midwives and professional status.' *British Journal of Midwifery*, Vol. 4, No. 10: 543–50.

Symon, A. (1997a). *The Rise and Fall of Perinatal Litigation: A Medico-legal Examination of Allegations of Negligence in Childbirth since 1980*. Ph.D. thesis, University of Edinburgh.

Symon, A. (1997b). 'Midwives and litigation: Supervision.' *British Journal of Midwifery*, Vol. 5: 70–72.

Symon, A. (1997c). 'Midwives and litigation: The importance of cardiotocographs'. *British Journal of Midwifery*, Vol. 5: 192–94.

Symon, A. (1997d). 'Midwives and litigation: The importance of communication'. *British Journal of Midwifery*, Vol. 5: 565–67.

Symon, A. (1997e). 'Midwives and litigation: Apologies and Explanations'. *British Journal of Midwifery*, Vol. 5: 594–96.

Symon, A. (1998). 'Midwives and litigation: motives for litigation. *British Journal of Midwifery*, Vol. 6: 12–14.

Symonds, E. (1985). 'Litigation in obstetrics and gynaecology'. *British Journal of Obstetrics and Gynaecology*, Vol. 92: 433–34.

Symonds, E. (1992). 'Medico-legal aspects.' In: Shaw, Soutters, Staunton (Eds). *Gynaecology* Edinburgh: Churchill Livingstone.

Taylor, A. (1994). 'Familiarity breeds contentment.' *Nursing Times*, Vol. 90, No.: 40–44.

Tew, M. (1985). 'Place of birth and perinatal mortality'. *Journal of the Royal College of General Practitioners*, Vol. 35: 390–94.

Tew, M. (1986). 'Do obstetric intranatal interventions make birth safer?' *British Journal of Obstetrics and Gynaecology*, Vol. 93: 659–74.

Tharmaratnam, S., Gillmer, M. (1995). 'The litigation boom in obstetrics.' *Obstetrics and Gynaecology Today*, Vol. 6, (2): 17–20.

Thomison, J. (1991). 'The obstetric dwindles'. *Southern Medical Journal,* Vol. 84: 943–44.

Thomson, A. (1991). 'Providing care at a midwives' antenatal clinic.' In: Robinson, S., Thomson, A. (Eds). *Midwives, Research and Childbirth Vol. 2*. London: Chapman and Hall.

Truelove, A. (1985). 'On handling complaints'. *Hospital and Health Services Review,* (Sept.): 229–32.

Tucker, J., Hall, M., Howie, P., Reid, M., Barbour, R., Florey, C., McIlwaine, G. (1996). 'Should obstetricians see women with normal pregnancies? A multicentre randomised controlled trial of routine antenatal care given by general practitioners and midwives compared with shared care led by obstetricians'. *British Medical Journal*, Vol. 312: 554–59.

Turnbull, D., McGinley, M., Fyvie, H., Johnstone, I., Holmes, A., Shields, N., Cheyne, H., MacLennan, B. (1995). 'The implementation and evaluation of the Midwifery Development Unit at Glasgow Royal Maternity Hospital'. *British Journal of Midwifery*, Vol. 3: 465–68.

UK Health Departments (1996) *Report on Confidential Enquiries into Maternal Deaths in the United Kingdom 1991–93*. London: HMSO.

UKCC [United Kingdon Central Council for Nursing, Midwifery and Health Visiting] (1989). *Exercising Accountability*. London: UKCC.

van den Berg, P., Schmidt, S., Gesche, J., Saling, E. (1987). 'Fetal distress and the condition of the newborn using cardiotocography and fetal blood analysis during labour'. *British Journal of Obstetrics and Gynaecology*, Vol. 94: 72–75.

Vincent, C., Martin, T., Ennis, M. (1991). 'Obstetric accidents: the patient's perspective'. *British Journal of Obstetrics and Gynaecology*, Vol. 98: 390–95.

Vincent, C., Young, M., Phillips, A. (1994a). 'Why do people sue doctors? A study of patients and relatives taking legal action'. *Lancet*, 343: 1609–13.

Vincent, C., Bark, P., Jones, A., Oliveri, L. (1994b). 'The impact of litigation on obstetricians and gynaecologists.' *Journal of Obstetrics and Gynaecology*, Vol. 14: 381–87.

Walker, P. (1995). 'Obstetricians should be included in integrated team care.' *British Medical Journal*, Vol. 310: 36–37.

Wall, J. (1991). (Ed) *'Compensation and Accountability – keeping the balance'*. Proceedings of MDU conference, 13.5.91.

Warden, J. (1996). 'NHS repeats its mistakes.' *British Medical Journal*, Vol. 312: 1247.

Waterson, J. (1993). 'Keeping Mum'. *Health Service Journal*, 20th May 1993: 27.

Whelan, C. (1988). 'Litigation and complaints procedures: objectives, effectiveness and alternatives'. *Journal of Medical Ethics*, Vol. 14: 70–76.

Wilkerson, V. (1984). 'The use of episiotomy in normal delivery'. *Midwives Chronicle*, Vol. 97 (1155): 106–10.

Witz, A. (1992). *Professions and Patriarchy*. London: Routledge.

Woolf, Lord (Chairman) (1996). *Access to Justice*. Final Report to the Lord Chancellor on the civil justice system in England and Wales. London: Lord Chancellor's Department.

Appendix A

The Midwifery Survey and Characteristics of the Respondents

The survey

Since a substantial majority (an estimated 85–90%) of midwives belong to the RCM, this seemed the most effective way of identifying them, particularly in Scotland, which has a scattered population with a significant number of midwives not living close to the urban centres where most maternity units are sited.

The Scottish board of the RCM has membership lists which can be broken down by branch; all full members were contacted. The Scottish RCM membership number (placed on the back of the return envelope) was used to identify non-responders, and also allowed return rates by branch to be calculated. RCM membership was also used to contact the midwives in one of the two English areas (from a list supplied by the London office of the RCM those with a particular post code were identified); the midwives in the second English area were those with a base within a particular city hospital which organizes community-based teams as well as hospital care. The midwifery management in this hospital sent me coded numbers for each of their midwives.

For the main survey 3,616 midwives were contacted: 372 in England, and 3,244 in Scotland. This followed a pilot survey of 48 midwives in one Scottish area which elicited an overall 71% return rate. All the questionnaires in Scotland were sent out by the RCM office in Edinburgh, and RCM membership numbers were used to identify non-responders. Questionnaires for the two English areas were distributed locally having been sent in bulk; in the case of the first English area the RCM membership list provided names and addresses, but the majority, who were hospital based, received their questionnaire in the internal mail; in the second English area the coded list provided by the midwifery management was used and the forms were again distributed in the internal mail. Each form came with a cover letter by the author, and a second cover letter from the Director of the Scottish board of the RCM encouraging midwives to participate; a Freepost envelope using the Edinburgh RCM office as a mailbox was included for the return of the questionnaires.

The cover letter assured respondents that their replies (and particularly comments) would be anonymised in any report, and this I have done. A small proportion of respondents interpreted this as meaning that the entire survey was anonymous, and they removed their unique identifier from the return envelope. This complicated the sending of reminders.

Reminders were sent out to the majority (80%) of non-responders; the process of identifying and targeting non-responders was complicated by the postal strike of May 1995. An initial response rate of 50% was used in calculating the costs of the survey (the pilot survey of 48 midwives in one part of Scotland produced an initial return rate of 42%, rising to 71% following reminders). For the main part of the survey, the initial return rate was 35%. Reminder letters included a copy of the questionnaire with a new cover letter, and a further Freepost envelope. Research costs from the National Board for Scotland (Margaret Callum Rodger Award), once obtained, did not quite allow for every non-responder to be sent a reminder.

Although a total of 3,616 questionnaires were sent out, the final sample population was slightly smaller than this, due to several members of the RCM having either retired or gone abroad, or having written saying they felt themselves ineligible, or who were otherwise uncontactable. When these numbers were removed from the study population, a total of 3,513 were left. A total of 1,805 completed questionnaires were returned, but the last 15 were rather slow in coming in (the last arrived in April 1998, three years after being sent), so analysis was of 1,790 replies, giving a response rate of 51%.

It is acknowledged that the English-based sub-sample is much smaller than the Scottish sub-sample, and so their replies may not be as replicable; however there is no reason to believe that the English respondents are atypical of English midwives generally.

The back page of the midwifery survey was left free for respondents to add whatever they felt like, either adding comments to answers given, discussing litigation (or the threat of litigation) and its effects on practice, or relating personal experiences in this field. In all 435 (24%) added comments on the back page, some spilling over onto extra sheets. One midwife included more than three typed sheets which she entitled 'The Ramblings of a Geriatric Midwife'. These are replicated in Appendix C.

Characteristics of midwifery respondents

Each midwife was asked for her grade, length of experience, number of deliveries carried out on average each year, and place of work. These are shown in Tables A1a–1d. Not all figures add up to the total number of returned questionnaires because many respondents left certain parts of the form blank. This also applies to all of the questions. This information allowed responses to be analysed (using cross tabulation in Microsoft ®Excel) by grade, size of unit in which practising, length of experience, and, where appropriate, by area of work.

It is not possible to draw a rural/urban distinction based on a respondent's stated size of unit, or area of work: some Community staff belonging to principally or wholly urban RCM branches cited the delivery rate of their local consultant unit, while others estimated what was presumably the delivery rate for Community staff in their area. Most RCM branches also have both rural and urban based members, and so branch membership alone cannot be used to draw this distinction; the situation is made more complicated because some respondents based in midwife-run units (MRUs) gave the annual delivery rate for the MRU (always less than a thousand), while others gave the delivery rate for the attached consultant unit.

The numbers of respondents in each of these categories is shown here.

Tables A1a – A1d:
Characteristics of midwifery respondents

1a Grade		1b Size of Unit (dels per year)	
D	7	Less than 100	103
E	631	100–999	114
F	497	1000–1999	275
G	539	2000–2999	295
H	28	3000–3999	240
I	22	4000–4999	176
Manager	8	5000 or more	366
Independent	2		
Lecturer	35		
Unspecified	25		

1c Length of experience (years)		1d Area of work	
Less than 3	191	Antenatal/postnatal/clinics	283
3 – 5.9	295	Community	307
6 – 8.9	275	Labour ward	353
9 – 11.9	298	Neonatal unit	179
12 – 14.9	158	Team/rotation	467
15 – 19.9	210		
20 or more	321		

Length of experience of respondents working in different areas and in different sized units was analysed to note any variation which might influence answers. In fact there were some significant differences found, as Table A2 shows.

Table A2:

Length of experience (in years): by size of unit and area of work

	mean	SD		mean	SD
Less than 100	14.12	8.27	Antenatal/Postnatal/Clinics	10.89	8.18
100–999	13.94	8.58	Community	14.52	7.79
1000–1999	12.38	7.79	Labour ward	10.83	7.55
2000–2999	10.97	7.89	Neonatal Unit	11.38	7.27
3000–3999	9.66	7.25	Team/Rotation	9.24	7.42
4000–4999	11.26	7.35			
5000 or more	10.03	7.61			

It can be seen that the mean length of experience differs especially between the smallest units (less than 100 deliveries a year) and those with 3,000–3,999 deliveries a year, and between those working on the Community and those in Team/Rotation schemes. However F-tests using Microsoft Excel showed the variance to be statistically significant between those working in units of 100–999 deliveries a year and those in units of 3,000–3,999 ($F = .033$): it will be seen that the standard deviation (and therefore the variance) is greater in these units than in the smallest units.

Analysis of variance (Anova) tests (also using Microsoft Excel) showed both Tables to be statistically significant, indicating that the populations of each sub-group are not identical, when analysed by length of experience at least. This should be borne in mind when responses by area of work and size of unit are shown in this report, since length of experience can be a confounding variable.

Scottish-English sub-sample

In addition to reporting responses by grade, length of experience, size of unit, and area of work, a comparison between the views expressed by midwives in Scotland and those in the two English areas was carried out. To do this midwives were 'matched' in pairs to exclude possibly confounding variables. The English sample being much smaller, it was taken as a base, and matching pairs for each respondent sought from within the Scottish sample.

Incidentally the response rates in the midwifery survey from Scotland and England were significantly different: 50% from the Scottish target population, compared to 63% from the English. This is partly explained by more effective targeting of reminders, but even the initial return rates, at 34% and 51% respectively, showed a significant difference.

Two hundred and thrity-one respondents comprised the English sample, but in 24 of these cases background data was partially missing and so matching could not be done.

Of the remaining 207, exact matches in terms of grade, length of experience, size of unit and area of work was possible in 139 cases (65% of the total sample); further matches were made possible by allowing some leeway in terms of grade, since it was evident that certain differences were present in the two respective samples, as shown below.

It appears that grading structures have not been identical within the two countries: while for the E grades there was little difference, for F and G grades length of experience was significantly shorter in England (calculation by Anova).

Table A3:
Comparison of length of experience of different grades

		Scotland	England	
E grades	*mean (years)*	6.63	6.08	
	SD	5.87	6.23	N/S
	n =	563	68	
F grades	*mean (years)*	12.16	8.87	
	SD	6.74	8.12	$p < 0.01$
	n =	435	51	
G grades	*mean (years)*	16.14	13.07	
	SD	7.52	7.25	$p < 0.001$
	n =	438	90	

Given these differences, a difference of one grade (e.g. F to G) was allowed in seeking a match for an English respondent when an exact match was not possible. Similarly, some difference in terms of length of experience was allowed: for between 5 and 10 years, a difference of up to three years was allowed (e.g. 5 compared with 8); for 10 to 15 years a difference of up to 4 years; and above 15 years a difference of up to 6 years.

This meant that pairing was possible in 172 cases in all, 74.5% of the total sample, or for 83% of those who provided the necessary background data. In this report, where applicable, reference is made to any significant differences between the Scottish-English matched pairs.

Appendix B

The Obstetric Survey
and Characteristics of the Respondents

The survey

Obstetricians were approached using the published list of Fellows and Members of the Royal College of Obstetricians and Gynaecologists (RCOG), and through names supplied by the RCOG and by the hospitals concerned. Practitioners were targeted at their last known place of work; because of job mobility a number of junior grade practitioners were uncontactable, and so this survey contains a large proportion of senior obstetricians.

As with the midwifery questionnaire, the English sub-sample is much smaller than the Scottish sub-sample; nevertheless, a number of statistically significant differences were found. The caveat about the size of the English-based midwifery sub-sample applies to these English-based obstetricians too.

Those targeted for this survey were all those thought to be practising obstetrics in Scottish hospitals and in the three hospitals which are included within the two English areas; also targeted were a number of GPs in Scotland who practise obstetrics outwith the consultant unit setting in rural/island areas. The cover letter which accompanied the survey form specified that the research concerns obstetrics and not gynaecology, since this reflects the data collection from legal files; since many early pregnancy conditions are treated in gynaecology wards and not on maternity wards in some hospitals, for the purposes of this survey 'obstetrics' is deemed to be from the 20th week of pregnancy onwards. Each questionnaire came with a cover letter from the author guaranteeing absolute confidentiality, and indicating supervision from a senior Scottish obstetrician; also included was a stamped addressed envelope for responses to be sent to the offices of the RCOG in London, who kindly allowed me to use their address as a post box.

A total of 338 questionnaires were sent, and the initial response rate was 52% (n = 174); reminders, including a cover letter and a further stamped address envelope, were sent to all non-responders, and this produced a total response rate of 63% (n = 211). Seven were returned indicating that the respondent was in some way unable to take part. The questionnaire had been piloted using obstetricians from one hospital in Scotland; following this, and discussions with the supervising obstetrician, the format was revised for the main survey. The survey was funded by a postgraduate studentship from the Economic and Social Research Council (ESRC) which paid university fees and made a small contribution to research costs.

In an attempt to maximize the response rate, the obstetric survey form was slightly shorter than the midwifery survey form, and no free space was left on which extra comments could be added. It is acknowledged that the discussion of the various points raised in the questionnaires leans more to the views of midwives, since far fewer additional comments by obstetricians were received.

Characteristics of obstetric respondents

Two hundred and eleven obstetricians responded; 21 from the three English hospitals, 190 from Scotland.

Table B1:
Grade of obstetric respondents

	England	Scotland
Consultant	10	82
Senior Registrar	3	24
Staff Grade	–	13
Registrar	6	38
SHO	2	9
Research etc.	–	5
GP	–	19

The GPs were based in three towns in mainland Scotland away from the central belt, and in three towns on the Scottish islands. The SHOs were those who were identified either by the RCOG or their respective hospitals as being 'career obstetricians' – i.e. were not GP trainees; 21 respondents came from the three English hospitals.

Comparisons between the various sub-groups was carried out using Anova in Microsoft Excel and Chi-square tests. Given the relatively small sizes of these sub-groups, only one statistically significant difference in their background data was found in their characteristics.

English staff claimed on average to work 55 hours a week; Scottish hospital staff 61 hours ($p < 0.1$); Scottish GPs claimed to work 63 hours a week. Comparing all staff in the English and Scottish consultant units, there is no significant difference in length of experience, the averages being 11.5 and 14 years respectively ($p < 0.1$). For the 10 English and 81 Scottish consultants, there is no significant difference in their length of experience (18 and 21.5 years respectively; $p < 0.1$). The English staff claimed on average to deliver 119 babies a year, compared with 97 for Scottish consultant unit staff ($p < 0.1$). The Scottish GPs gave estimated personal delivery rates of between 0 and 50, with an average of 15.

The English staff came from three units with estimated annual delivery rates of about 1,400, 3,100 and 6,400 (average for English respondents 4,230); the Scottish hospital-based staff (with the exception of a small DGH with a delivery rate of 450) came from units with estimated rates of between 1,200 and 5,600 (average for Scottish respondents 3,328). This produced the one statistically significant result ($p < .05$), which may be notable in terms of a respondent's likelihood of becoming involved – however peripherally – in litigation, if it is taken that a larger unit is more likely to attract legal complaints. This does not of course mean that an individual is necessarily more likely to be involved personally, only that the unit in which they work may be more likely to be the target of a complaint.

Appendix C

'The Ramblings of a Geriatric Midwife'

The following was attached by one respondent to the questionnaire form.

My earlier years as a midwife were spent, as was the norm at that time, as a much more independent practitioner, delivering both at home and in hospital.

The home confinements, though often carried out in the most appalling conditions, seemed to be easier, less painful, quicker and seldom complicated, although most of the mums were multiparous. Patients did, however, expect to experience some pain during their labour and childbirth. On the very odd occasions when the outcome was not satisfactory – for example a stillbirth, as sometimes did happen – there was never any question of 'suing or laying the blame'. It was assumed by all concerned that everyone had done their best, and a routine investigation was carried out into the case and its outcome. Perhaps it had been the fault of the mother – possibly calling the midwife out too late for a breech delivery: the body already born, no pulsation present in the cord and the head trapped in the transverse behind a not fully dilated cervix when the midwife arrived. Perhaps it could have been mismanagement at some point in the care by the midwife. It somehow did not seem to be so important whose fault, if anyone's, it was – the outcome was the same, and was accepted as a fact of life.

It was generally accepted that childbirth was not always 100% successful and the desired outcome – a healthy mother and baby – could not always be guaranteed. This is still a fact of life, though today's clients seem to see it as their right to have 100% successful childbirth, and if something does not go according to plan then 'someone must pay' – usually in money terms – safe childbirth can never be guaranteed!

Hospital deliveries were rarely overseen by the medical staff and often the patients did not see the doctor until the postnatal period, which was of course much longer then. The majority of patients were admitted, assessed and delivered without ever seeing a doctor. CTGs were obviously not in use then, but fetal heart irregularities and thus fetal distress could be picked up quite easily by the frequent use of the Pinards stethoscope. What is now termed 'early' or 'late' decelerations could be detected and acted upon as seemed fit at the time.

I do not think for a moment that one should 'harp' back to the 'old days', but I do sometimes wonder if they were so bad after all. True, the patients were not so well informed, nor were they so willing to take such an active part in their care as nowadays, but it does seem that they had fewer mishaps and far less complicated labours when they agreed – following discussion of course – to allow the carer to 'Do what you think is best.'

I am very much in favour of progress and taking full advantage of all the equipment and expertise available today to help ensure the safe confinement of all mums and the delivery of healthy babies.

It has been suggested that reverting back to more home confinements is the way forward. In many ways I agree and as already noted those I attended at home seemed to have easier times. Things however have changed since then – the extended family is no longer to the fore, the ever present Granny of yesteryear is today probably out at work! This role, however, may now be partly taken over by the husband or partner who is much more involved in all aspects of childbirth than previously. Where, I wonder, does the midwife of today stand where back up services are concerned? Who provides her back up on district? Is it totally given by the GP? Will all hospitals have an organized Flying Squad? Or will the paramedics fill the bill? Are there enough paramedics to man every ambulance? Are they already qualified in midwifery and neonatology? Some clients stay quite a distance from the hospitals and as centralisation continues they may be even further removed. 'Transfer her in,' they say. If bleeding or a prolapsed cord is present, time is of the essence. Where will the midwife stand then? How will litigation affect her in these circumstances? Must she learn to stabilize her patient? Will she be qualified to cannulate and then administer IV fluids in order to alleviate her client's condition before 'official' assistance arrives?

The resuscitation of the newborn is another area which seems to hold many of the potential pitfalls for the Community Midwife of today. The majority of cases will no doubt be fine, but think of the number of unexpected 'Crash calls' put out for neonatal resuscitation in hospital, and one must assume that a few such cases must occur at home. Where will the midwife stand? Will she carry oxygen at all times, along with A 'Bag and Mask'? How often must she update her skills in neonatal resuscitation? Will she carry any drugs? Will she be trained to intubate? Trained to administer IPPV via an ET tube? Is her back up a paediatric flying squad with a ventilator or a paramedic? 'Transfer her to hospital' will again be the cry, but time is of the essence in these circumstances, and is a commodity she does not have!

In times gone by the midwife had a mucous extractor and a drug to counteract any analgesia the mother may have had. The mothers were aware of this and knew there was little else available, either in or out of hospital. Now, however, they know that oxygen can be given, that many different drug stimulants etc. can be given – Adrenaline, Soda Bicarbonate, Dextrose, IV therapy can be initiated, blood gases can be checked and assisted ventilation given by headbox, nasal CPAP, or full ventilation by ET tube as required, thus reducing the risk of hypoxia and brain damage. Parents are now well informed and aware of the advances made in neonatology in recent years – much of this information gained through the media.

These facilities cannot obviously be provided at home but any mother whose baby is in need of them is sure to ask the question 'Why not?' How is the midwife then placed? Should the carer have anticipated the outcome and transferred the patient to hospital earlier – an easy decision with hindsight, but difficult at the time without the aid of CTG tracings, probably no early ARM to check the colour of the liquor, or no benefit of scalp pHs if the fetal heart (rate) seemed suspect on auscultation. There is probably little that the midwife could anticipate as so many of these babies who are 'flat' are unexpectedly so. That however is going to be of little consolation to the parents who are going to have a damaged baby at bets, or at worst a neonatal death or stillbirth as a result.

At present it would appear that arrangements for back up services, particularly for outlying districts, are extremely sketchy and any person opting to offer home confinements midwifery services to such areas will be very vulnerable indeed, and may be leaving themselves open to the possibility of massive litigation.

Perhaps the Domino delivery system would alleviate many of these potential problems. The medical assistance and equipment would be on hand if required (most likely at or just following delivery) for both mother and baby. If there were no 'hiccoughs' both mum and baby could return home just a few hours after delivery.

If actual home births – especially in outlying areas a good distance from hospital – are to be encouraged the midwife and the patient must be very sure how they both stand before making their 'Informed choice'. Perhaps there could be the possibility of the parents signing a disclaimer if the midwife is at all unhappy at the situation.

Being a midwife today can be very rewarding but it also carries frightening responsibilities. Might it be wise therefore to discuss the litigation aspect in much more detail before the autonomy of the midwife of today is further developed.